StartU Saturday

WORKBOOK

A week-by-week guide
to starting a business

Emma Jones

that was easy:

A Brightword book
www.brightwordpublishing.com

HARRIMAN HOUSE LTD
3A Penns Road
Petersfield
Hampshire
GU32 2EW
GREAT BRITAIN

Tel: +44 (0)1730 233870
Fax: +44 (0)1730 233880
Email: enquiries@harriman-house.com
Website: www.harriman-house.com
First published in Great Britain in 2011
Copyright © Harriman House Ltd

ISBN: 978-1-908003-12-6

British Library Cataloguing in Publication Data
A CIP catalogue record for this book can be obtained from the British Library.

Book printed and bound in the UK by CPI Antony Rowe

Set in Georgia and Giza Five Five

About the Author

Emma Jones is a business expert and author, and founder of small business support company Enterprise Nation. Her books include *Spare Room Start Up* and *Working 5 to 9* (Harriman House), *Go Global* and *The Start-Up Kit* (Brightword Publishing).

Following a five-year career at an international accounting firm, Emma started her first business at 27, from a spare room in her Manchester apartment. That business was sold 18 months later, and the experience led to Emma's next venture, Enterprise Nation.

Its website (www.enterprisenation.com) was launched in 2006 and became the most popular for home business owners in the UK, attracting over 100,000 visitors each month.

Emma Jones

Enterprise Nation has evolved to help even more would-be entrepreneurs. The company now offers books, kits, online tools, content, friendly forums, video clips and weekly courses designed to help anyone start and grow a small business.

Emma advises the government on small business issues and is one of the founders of national campaign, StartUp Britain. Her vision is to ensure anyone in the UK thinking of starting a business has the tools at their disposal to turn their dream into profitable and fulfilling reality.

In partnership with training company CragRats, Enterprise Nation is the company delivering StartUp Saturday to you!

Welcome to StartUp Saturday!

Presented in 11 clear, week-by-week sections (the last week is a StartUp celebration and time for any final questions if you attend the 12-week course), this workbook offers all the tools, tips and templates you need to successfully find an idea and turn it into a way of making a living. Work through the sections with guidance from a trainer during a class, or on your own in the comfort of your own home.

Scribble in it, travel with it and eat tea whilst reading it – this workbook will help you move from start-up to successful business owner.

There is extra support on offer at www.enterprisenation.com where you will find useful content, friendly forums and daily video clips to help you start and grow your business. Have your online questions answered via the site or make the most of the weekly opportunity to discuss ideas face to face with your trainer and classmates.

The classes themselves will be informative as well as fun! They are delivered by leading educational company CragRats with a team of trainers who are passionate about engaging and inspiring audiences to achieve their full potential.

Enjoy the workbook and your StartUp Saturday experience!

PS. If you'd like to tweet your way through the book – or live from classes – and share with others the tips you're picking up, please use the hashtag #StartUpSaturday and follow @SUpSaturday – find out how to tweet in Week 9 and on page 149!

> **"We're delighted to be helping the next generation of entrepreneurs and hope that StartUp Saturday will play a key role in turning great ideas into real businesses."**
>
> **— Andrew Gabriel, UK Managing Director, Staples**

contents

Introduction

Each year over 270,000 people start a business and become their own boss and there's never been a better time to start.

Why? Because it's now perfectly possible to start and grow a successful business in your spare time, from home, and on a budget. In this workbook we'll show you how it's done.

People in their thousands are spotting gaps in the market or turning a passion/hobby/skill into a way of making a living. They are embracing free or low-cost technology to promote themselves and make sales, with a good number of these sales coming from overseas customers. Having access to the internet means you can start a business on a Monday and be easily trading with the world by Wednesday.

The start-up companies profiled in the workbook discuss how they got going at low risk and low cost. They are selling everything from baby hats to London Mini tours, business consultancy and party cakes. Their products may be different, but the point in common is that they all talk about how much they are relishing the freedom and flexibility that comes with being their own boss and the exciting times ahead with new products, partnerships and contracts on the way.

If you'd like to experience this, all you have to do is follow some basic steps: come up with an idea, do some research and marketing, offer a good customer service and, quite literally (almost before you know it) you're in business!

With this workbook you also receive help from our host sponsor, Staples. Each week at StartUp Saturday, Staples will be extending offers on products ranging from business cards to office furnishings.

With the steps, tips and templates in the workbook, and weekly offers in-store, you have all you need to start a business. And if you come along to StartUp Saturday, you'll meet others in the same position – meaning plenty of chances to swap notes and share ideas.

Let's get started on what will be an exciting week-by-week journey.

Emma Jones

emma@enterprisenation.com
@emmaljones
www.enterprisenation.com

Acknowledgements

With thanks to the profiled start-ups for allowing their stories to be told:

Arianna Cadwallader	Saturday Sewing Session
Roya Dabir-Alai, Nicky Croxford, Trisha Champaneri	Sitting in a Tree
Ella Gascoigne	Startup PR
Tracy Gray	Button and Bean
Alex Hardie	How do you do Marketing
Laura Helps	Cakes by Laura
Oliver Knight, Robert Welch, Alastair Bruton	SmallcarBIGCITY
John and Moi Lakey	Candlelight Creations
Tim Latham	Unconsultancy
Nick Proctor	Amber Energy Consultants
Hayley Ramm	Squigglers
Kim Scott	Hats My Baby
Caroline Stevens	Ounces2Pounds

With thanks to expert contributors:

Emily Hewett	Birds on the Blog
Jackie Wade	Winning Sales
Louise Findlay-Wilson	PrPro
Mark Shaw	Twitter expert
San Sharma	Enterprise Nation
Dan Wilson	eBay expert
Joanna Tall	Offtoseemylawyer.com

And also to the StartUp Saturday partners:

Staples	www.staples.co.uk
CragRats	www.cragrats.com

Week 1

Uncover your BIG idea and research the market

As with any undertaking, preparation is key. Whether baking a cake, going on a date or heading on holiday, time is given over to research and preparation. Starting a business is no different. Dedicate time to coming up with an idea and ensuring it's viable through market research. These are the base ingredients required for a successful enterprise!

Coming Up With an Idea

Ingredient number one: a business idea! Many people tell me they would like to start a business but what's holding them back is not having an idea. It's easy to come up with one. Ask yourself these three questions:

Firstly, is there a gap in the market?

Have you tried to buy something that you just can't find? Could others be looking for the same thing? If so, this presents a market opportunity. Have you ever wondered 'why doesn't such a product exist?' or 'why isn't a particular service available?' – if so, it's time for you to plug that gap!

Arianna Cadwallader spotted a gap in the market when she saw sewing events successfully taking shape across London but with nothing in her area. She decided to do something about it and Saturday Sewing Session is the result.

CASE STUDY

Name: Arianna Cadwallader

Business: Saturday Sewing Session

Started: July 2010

At the age of 29, Arianna Cadwallader is a maker and milliner specialising in bespoke wedding dresses and head pieces.

"Although my head is in the 21st century, my heart is firmly in the 1940s. I have a passion for skills that are not used so much anymore; quilting, knitting, sewing, crochet and dressmaking."

With this love of craft and all things handmade, Arianna wanted to create a workshop that would encourage modern women (and men!) to learn a new skill in a creative environment. She wanted to show how, with a few basic skills and some fabric, you can be creative and modern and make something for yourself or others to treasure. To achieve this, she launched 'Saturday Sewing Session', after seeing a number of similar successful ventures and spotting a gap in the market in her area.

She first came to the attention of Enterprise Nation after submitting an entry to the Ideas 101 competition run in conjunction with PayPal. Her entry shows just how inventive you can be when operating on a budget.

"I have managed to secure a great room above the Chelsea Ram pub with a beautiful long table and lots of light. Talking to the manager, I secured the room for free and together we worked out a reasonably priced lunch menu for the ladies and gents who will attend, so that they will gain business on what is generally a quiet lunchtime period for them (not to mention the drinks afterwards, too).

"I have also secured a partnership with Battersea sewing centre for the hire of machines at half price. The sewing centre will advertise for me and in my session I will advertise his shop for all repairs/new machines for anyone who falls in love with this skill. I am also in the process of getting a deal with a gorgeous cake shop where potentially they could supply all the cakes for a good price and I will promote them in return."

Arianna is successfully up and running, with Saturday classes fully booked for six months, more classes on the way, and plenty more promotion on the way.

"I am in *Time Out* online, I have a Twitter account, Facebook page and blog and I distribute flyers in places my target audience go. I send out emails to my database and attend start-up business events to network. I have got some upcoming promotion in online and hard-copy magazines and I email relevant companies to see if they are interested in coming onboard."

Arianna's plans for the next 12 months involve extending the classes to more days and more subjects. Having graduated from Wimbledon School of Arts with a degree in costume interpretation, this young entrepreneur is inviting many of her classmates to come and teach, as they specialise in different areas and have individual skills to share. Arianna gives credit to this network of friends and family in helping achieve her goals.

"My boyfriend is an expert in marketing and has brilliant organisational skills. The support from him and my friends and family has been unwavering; they help me prioritise class schedules, materials, ideas for workshops and build up business relationships. They are my constant source of inspiration."

Arianna is passionate about making her idea happen and excited about where this business journey will lead.

- **www.saturdaysewingsession.co.uk**
  @SatSewSession

Secondly, what is my passion/hobby/skill?

Many people are turning what they love into a way of making a living. Best of all, when you work on what you enjoy doing it never really feels like work! Are you a dab hand at DIY? Have an eye for photography? A head for figures? These skills and hobbies can easily be turned into a business as you offer products or services to friends and family – they tell others – and before you know it, you're in business!

This is what happened to Laura Helps, who turned a passion for baking into a tasty profit with her spare-time business, Cakes by Laura.

CASE STUDY

Name: Laura Helps

Business: Cakes by Laura

Started: March 2010

Laura Helps was working from home as a customer services officer and, in her spare time, liked to cook and bake. She decided to try her hand at making and decorating a Christmas cake.

"It was the ugliest cake you've ever seen but it sparked a passion. So I baked, and decorated, and soon got to the point where I was being asked to make cakes for friends and family. News of my work got passed on via word of mouth and Cakes by Laura was born!"

To ensure she was health-and-safety-checked to cook in the kitchen and sell the finished item, Laura ordered the 'Safer Food, Better Business' pack from the Food Standards Agency and worked through the items that applied to her activity (which wasn't much, as cakes are so low risk). She then called the local Environmental Health department, who sent an officer to check working conditions in the kitchen.

"We talked about the risks; she had a look around the kitchen, and passed me, subject to completing a Food Hygiene certificate, which I did."

With her first few customers being friends and family, Laura then started to secure orders via her website – which now accounts for 80% of orders.

"I spend time every week uploading new photos to the site and changing the content. I also use Facebook and Twitter to try and create a buzz around my products. Word of mouth is my second-biggest promoting tool and it's completely free!"

Laura has invested in a sign-covered van and she's often stopped in the car park and asked about her business. She attends shows and fairs and is working towards the business being a full-time occupation. When this happens, her plan is to move out of the home kitchen and into commercial premises.

In terms of advice for others looking to tread the same path, Laura has this to say:

"Research, research, and when you're done, research some more. Read as much as you can about running your own business; ask questions of people currently running a business, as their experience may prove invaluable. But most of all – enjoy it! It's so rewarding to see your business grow."

- **www.cakesbylaura.co.uk**
  @cakesbylaura

Thirdly, is there something someone else is doing that I can do better myself?

If you've bought something and been unimpressed, why not step in, set up in business, and provide a better offer? Many good ideas stem from spotting products and services that can be improved upon. Think about whether you could package a product in a better way, offer a service more efficiently or add an extra bell or whistle to make something that's rather ordinary, quite unique...

* * *

Your idea will develop over time. Don't be surprised if in 12 months' time it looks different to when you started out. This is okay and a natural result of refining the business and clarifying the market offer. What's important is to get started with the beginnings of an idea – there'll be time to develop it as you get feedback from customers and input from others.

Use the first template to come up with your idea.

Template 1: What's Your Big Idea?

Have I spotted a gap in the market?

What is my passion/hobby/skill?

Is there something I've seen someone else do that I can do better myself?

What about buying into someone else's idea via a franchise? (See page 14 for details.)

50 ideas for businesses

- Virtual PA
- Online information publisher
- Book publisher
- Magazine publisher
- Author
- Writer
- Blogger
- Social media website owner
- eBay trader
- Online store owner
- Giftware maker
- Giftware seller
- Artisan
- Cupcake maker
- Cosmetics producer
- Hair and make-up artist
- Origami artist
- Picture artist
- Furniture maker
- Jewellery designer
- Footwear designer
- Clothing producer
- Baby wear supplier
- Toymaker
- Children's party organiser
- Leisure & entertainment
- Musician
- Magician
- Beer producer
- Events organiser
- Party planner
- Mystery shopper
- Image consultant
- Personal development practitioner
- Fitness advisor
- Personal trainer
- Lifestyle advisor
- Homestager
- Photographer
- Accountant
- Lawyer
- Translator
- IT services
- Mobile applications developer
- Software developer
- Print and web designer
- Electrical reseller
- Network marketer
- Pet care
- Rare breed pig farmer

• •

Don't forget the friends and family focus group. Talk to family and friends and ask them where they think your talents lie. They might just help you discover your business idea in an area you hadn't thought of.

• •

There are so many ideas from which to choose (50 are noted on the previous page, and I have interviewed owners of all of them) that yours may be a problem of having too many ideas as opposed to none. In which case, spend time on lots of ideas and let the customer decide where you will specialise, i.e. whatever emerges as the most popular selling item.

Niche is nice

Not included. Think of including before worksheet.

When coming up with your idea, bear in mind that 'niche' businesses are often the best kind of businesses. What I mean by this is: come up with a product or service that meets the needs of a very well-defined audience. For example, set up as a translator focused on Spanish translation and helping UK companies break into Spanish speaking markets; or sell shoes specifically to people with big feet. There are two key benefits to having a niche business:

- you keep marketing costs low, as your audience is well defined; you know where your audience are and understand the kind of marketing messages to which they will respond

- customer loyalty remains high, as you become the expert in your field or the only provider of certain products; customers will want to stay with you and benefit from the specialist product or service you offer.

Katie Macdonald is a virtual PA (personal assistant). After she set up her business, she realised she had to define her offer and stand out with a 'unique selling point'; that point happened to be a specialism she loves:

> "When I first set up I didn't think I needed a niche as I considered the skills I had were so transferable that I could support anyone in any business sector. Then I came on to marketing my business and I didn't know where to start. After deciding on my niche market of providing VA [virtual assistant] services to companies in the food sector, everything fell into place. I have a focus to my business, and a focus which I happen to love. Finding my niche hasn't confined my business, it has specialised it."

The niche list

Here are some businesses I've come across that have benefited from having a clear niche

Company	Niche
Sarah J Thomas photography (**www.sarahjthomas.com**)	Maternity, newborn, baby and child photography
Collie Wobbles (**www.colliewobbles.co.uk**)	Border Collie/sheep dog related products
Rock N' Roll Bride (**www.rocknrollbride.com**)	Brides wanting a rock 'n' roll wedding
Worksnug (**www.worksnug.com**)	Mobile workers seeking connected spaces
Twins Store (**www.twins-store.co.uk**)	Advice and store for parents with twins
Pai Skincare (**www.paiskincare.com**)	Organic skincare for people with sensitive skin
Petite Cake Balls (**www.petitecakeballs.co.uk**)	An alternative to traditional cakes: bitesize cake balls
Peekaboo Communications (**www.peekaboocoms.co.uk**)	PR for companies selling baby-related products and services

Think about how you can fashion your idea so it has a clear purpose for a clearly defined audience.

• •

Whatever the idea, base the business on what you enjoy, what people will buy and maybe something that improves on what's already available.

• •

An idea as part of the package

If you've asked yourself the three key questions to come up with an idea but nothing really appeals, consider buying into someone else's idea. You can do so through buying a franchise or signing up as a party-plan consultant. Benefit from being your own boss whilst also having the support of a central team and the proven idea that comes with it!

Here are 30 top franchise or party-plan opportunities:

My Secret Kitchen	www.mysecretkitchen.co.uk
Jamie at Home	www.jamieathome.com
Pampered Chef	www.pamperedchef.co.uk
Girlie Gardening	www.girliegardening.com
Kleeneze	www.kleeneze.com
Pyjama Drama	www.pyjamadrama.com
Talking Tots	www.talkingtots.info
Raring2go	www.raring2go.co.uk
Neal's Yard	www.nealsyardremedies.com
Families Magazine	www.familiesonline.co.uk
Maid2Clean	www.maid2clean.co.uk
Razzamataz	www.razzamataz.co.uk
Best in Glass	www.best-in-glass.com
Harmony at Home	www.harmonyathome.co.uk
Ounces2Pounds	www.ounces2pounds.co.uk
Shoes Glorious Shoes	www.shoesgloriousshoes.co.uk
Travel Counsellors	www.travelcounsellors.co.uk
Tatty Bumpkin	www.tattybumpkin.com
Barrett & Coe	www.barrettandcoe.co.uk

Vie At Home	www.vieathome.com
Barking Mad	www.barkingmad.uk.com
Usborne Books	www.usborne.com
Thebestof	www.getthebestof.co.uk
Spanish Amigos	www.spanishamigos.co.uk
Kumon	www.kumon.co.uk
Tupperware	www.tupperware.co.uk
Music Bugs	www.musicbugs.co.uk
Poppy's Books	www.poppysbooks.co.uk
Stardust	www.stardustkids.co.uk
Captain Tortue Group	www.captaintortuegroup.com

CASE STUDY

Name: Caroline Stevens

Business: Ounces2Pounds

Started: April 2010

In the spring of 2009 Caroline Stevens was made redundant and started to think about working from home. It was at this time Caroline read an article about buying gold at parties. She searched online for the gold party company referred to in the article. This company was Ounces2Pounds and Caroline was happy to sign up as a representative, impressed by their professional image and positive profile.

"After the interview and meeting the managing director at their head office in London, I knew I could be a franchisee/party planner for this company. Buying and selling gold has an image of not being the most elegant of professions but Ounces2Pounds has changed that with its professionalism."

As a representative, Caroline hosts two to three parties a week, mainly in the evenings. Caroline is earning as much as she did when working in a job for four days a week and she now has time for home life, too.

"I promote my services at each party. Next to my gold-testing equipment I lay out my business card, 'host a gold party' card, and a 'book a party' sheet. Once I have finished the transaction I mention that the client can host their own party, briefly explain how the commission system works, and ask them if they would be interested. If they are, I take their name and number. I suggest I ring them in a week's time once they have had a chance to ask around friends, family, colleagues, etc. It has been very successful for me."

The beauty of being a representative is that Caroline is her own boss but can also count on support from the central team at Ounces2Pounds. The company offers training, dedicated IT support, help with administration and, most important, assistance with booking parties and offering moral support.

"I was lucky to find Ounces2Pounds as it offers me a way of working that fits my requirements and lifestyle perfectly. For anyone else considering becoming a party-plan representative, I would say you have to like and believe in the product or service. I truly enjoy what I am doing, so that selling smile comes naturally!"

- **www.ounces2pounds.com**
  @ounces2pounds

Researching the Market

You have your idea. To turn it into a business requires some market research. Here's how to go about it.

First, research your potential customers, the competition and a price point by visiting competitors' sites, online trade sites/forums, reading reports, and seeking intelligence from experts. Look for data and comments that will answer the following questions:

- What is the number of potential customers you can serve, and how do these customers like to be served?

- What are their characteristics, spending patterns and who are their key influencers?

- Who is currently serving your market?

- Where are your potential customers going for their goods and services?

- What do they like about what they're getting and, more importantly, what do they dislike (as this opens up opportunities for you to improve on the status quo)?

- In view of the above, what price can you charge for your product/service?

Price yourself at a rate that's competitive with other providers in the market, that takes into account the amount of time, personal service and added value you offer, and that will turn a profit at the end of the day!

TIP: The name game

Coming up with an idea and carrying out research will get you thinking about what to name your new baby (by which I mean your business!). If you are selling your knowledge, the company may be named after you – for example, 'Emma Jones Advisory Services'. In which case, job done. But if you're looking for something else, think of a name that:

- is easy to spell
- has an available domain name
- is not already registered with Companies House (use a free webcheck service to access existing company names at www.companieshouse.gov.uk)
- people will remember.

You might want to protect the name through a trademark. *See page 50 for information on how to go about that.*

Here are some of my favourite names:

- Urban Splash
- Apple
- Innocent
- Pret
- MOO.COM
- Twitter
- Etsy

Not all of them say what they do but they are sweet and simple.

If you get stuck coming up with something suitable, visit another company name I like – Bitsy – it's our site (so I'm a little biased!) but you will find people on Bitsy who can help you win the name game, as the site is buzzing with talented copywriters and wordsmiths.

Template 2: Market Research

How big is the market?

What is the number of potential customers I can serve and how do these customers like to be served?

What are their characteristics, spending patterns and who are their key influencers?

Who is currently serving my market?

Where are my potential customers currently going for their goods and services?

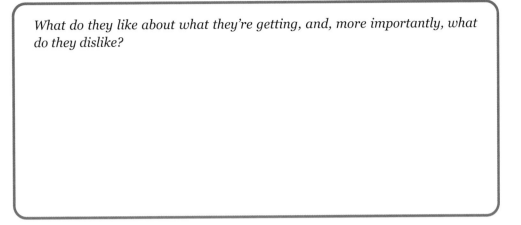

What do they like about what they're getting, and, more importantly, what do they dislike?

What price can I charge for my product/service?

What's competitive and takes into account the amount of time, personal service and added value that I offer?

- -

TIP: What am I worth?

How much do you think customers or clients would pay for your product or service? Take a look at how similar offerings are priced and talk to people about how much they'd be willing to pay. Then talk to suppliers to check you can source materials and deliver at a price that covers your costs.

Since starting a business from home (which we recommend you do!) will save you lots of money, you can pass some of these savings onto your customers. It will give you an edge over other businesses. But don't undercharge for the expertise and knowledge you offer.

Also, consider charging less for work that will reflect well on your business and boost your reputation, perhaps in the media or with a credible customer.

• •

Research tools

To find answers to your questions and to source intelligence on competitors, visit forums and sites where your potential customers gather and read up on the local competition. Locate these forums through Google searches and following links posted on social media sites such as Facebook and Twitter.

Visit competitor websites and consider buying from them, or using their service, so you can get an idea of their strong points – and maybe their weaknesses too.

Source primary or firsthand data by conducting a survey or posing questions via social media channels.

Survey tools

- SurveyMonkey
  www.surveymonkey.com

- Wufoo
  www.wufoo.com

Social media channels

- Twitter
  www.twitter.com

- Facebook
  www.facebook.com

- LinkedIn
  www.linkedin.com

Or hit the streets with a clipboard! This is what Hayley Ramm did when she wanted feedback on her idea for a painting class for kids.

CASE STUDY

Name: Hayley Ramm

Bsiness: Squigglers

Started: October 2010

The inspiration for Hayley Ramm's business came from four-year-old daughter Grace, who loves to paint. It got Hayley thinking about whether she could start a painting club and turn it into a business.

"I have spent many a day painting in the kitchen with Grace, and I wanted to turn this into a business where I could continue the fun but also gain some flexibility to fit around Grace's start at school."

Whilst employed as an HR consultant, Hayley started talking to parents and carers to get their feedback on the idea. After that she carried out market research through questionnaires in the local area to get some direction on the best dates, times, venues and pricing for her club. She also visited lots of competitors to gain a better understanding of what adults and children did or didn't want from an activity group.

The result is a company called Squigglers. And with its profile already in the local news, this company looks set to go down a treat in Hayley's area and beyond.

This business is a family affair; Hayley's husband helps with marketing, and daughter Grace attends painting clubs with Mum (when she's not at school!). It has been an exciting start, with Squigglers flyers delivered across her local area and a write-up in the local paper that led to Hayley and Grace being recognised on the school run the next day!

Hayley has had help from local business support agencies Tedco and South Tyneside Means Business, who helped with a business plan, cash flow forecast and funding applications.

Is Hayley pleased she made the move to self-employment?

"Most definitely. So far I have the three 'F's I always wished for: fun, flexibility and finance (well, the last one needs a little working on as you can imagine in these early months!)."

- **www.squigglers.co.uk**

Template 3: SWOT Analysis

With your idea, and now your research in-hand that supports it, prepare a SWOT analysis. This stands for: Strengths, Weaknesses, Opportunities, Threats.

Strengths

What are my strengths?

What can I do better than anyone else?

What resources do I have?

What's my unique selling point?

Weaknesses

What are my weaknesses?

What should I avoid?

Where do I lack skills?

What might hinder my success?

Opportunities

What opportunities do I see?

Does my idea tap into any trends?

Are there any emerging technologies that could help my idea?

Has there been anything in the news related to my idea?

Threats

What threats would I face?

Who's my competition?

Does changing technology affect my idea?

Complete this template to create your own SWOT Analysis.

Strengths

What are my strengths?

Weaknesses

What are my weaknesses?

Opportunities

What opportunities do I see?

Threats

What threats might I face?

Week 2

Five points to include in a business plan

After coming up with an idea and doing your research, writing a brief business plan is your first practical step to starting your business. With it under your belt you can say, "I'm off!"

I'M OFF

A business plan will act as your map; it will guide the business from start to growth, with reference to milestones along the way. For example, you might want to open a shop, launch a website or reach a number of customers within a certain time frame.

The plan will include information about how you intend to get started and what your ultimate objectives are – and how you aim to get from one to the other. You might want to start a business and sell it in a few years' time, or grow to a point where you wouldn't want to grow anymore. And, of course, you'll need to refer to resources: what you have already, what you'll need and how you'll pay for it.

You may also need a plan if you're looking to raise money, from friends or family, or from the bank.

With it in hand, you'll be off on your business journey.

Or IMOFF.

It's an easy way to remember the headings to include in your business plan: Idea, Market, Operations, Financials and Friends.

Idea

What's your idea?

Market

Who will be your customers or clients? And who is your competition?

Operations

How will you develop the idea, promote it, and provide good customer service?

Financials

Can you earn more than you spend, so that the business makes a profit? Do you need any funds to get started?

Friends

Do you have a support network on hand for when you need business advice? Are there complementary businesses you've identified with whom partnerships are a possibility?

Have these as headings in your plan and you've taken a big step closer to becoming your own boss.

- -

TIP: Re-visit regularly

Return to the plan to check progress against targets or to make amends as you respond to new opportunities. I re-visit the Enterprise Nation plan for a 'gentle' re-cap every six months and then at the start of each year I go away for a couple of days to re-read the plan, re-think the business, and re-write if required.

- -

Executive Summary
Summarise what's in the rest of the plan. Something like this:

The vision for ABC is to become the leading company for selling xxx to xxx. This plan sets out how the vision will be achieved in the period from 2011-2013. It outlines the product on offer, provides data on the customer market and shows how an experienced founder will have the company operating profitably within the first three months.

Having identified a clear gap in the market, I'm excited about the opportunity to start and build a successful business that will offer a quality product and service to a well defined market.

A. Smith
Founder, Company ABC

The Idea
Include here your 'elevator pitch'; what is your product and how will it benefit the customer?

This is the opportunity to explain the idea of the business in a few sentences.

* This title would be more like 'Advisory Board' if preparing the plan for a bank or funder.

The Market

Customers
Who will be your customers? Include the quantity of them, their demographic profile, geographic locations, social backgrounds; essentially any strong data that shows you know your audience.

Competition
Who is selling a similar product/service? How do you differ from them and what is your unique selling point?

You can do this by producing a table that lists the competition and you. Outline what makes you stand out in the market: is it that your service will be online, that you'll charge a different price, have an innovative marketing approach or offer the service with a special extra twist?

Operations

The CEO
You have come up with the idea for the business and you've done your research on the market. Now it's time for the reader to know a bit about you! Note your background, skills, experience and any credentials for running this business. Plus information on other key members of staff (if there are any).

Sourcing
If this applies to your business, refer to how you'll source your product/service. You may be making it yourself!

Sales & Marketing

How will you promote what you offer to your customers? Include a brief sales and marketing plan with headings like this:

Press – how many press releases do you plan to distribute each year and to which press channels: newspapers, magazines, radio, etc.?

Online – will you have your own blog/website? Mention other sites that you'll approach for reciprocal links.

Partners – what about marketing tie-ups with other companies selling to the same audience?

You know where your customers are, so let your marketing plan show that you'll reach them in print, online and even in the streets! [This topic will be covered in more detail in Week 8.]

Systems

You've sourced the service/product and told customers about it. Refer here to the process customers will go through to buy from you and the systems you'll have in place to deliver in time and on budget. Systems that may include online ordering and payment, a professional call-handling service to take orders or maybe some specific software. [Making sales and accepting payments will be covered in more detail in Week 7.]

Financials

Last but not least come the figures. Make this as clear as possible and it's probably best to do it in table form:

	Year 1	Year 2
Revenue		
Overheads		
Office rent		
Salary		
Stock		
Technology		
Marketing		
Travel & expenses		
Projected profit		

Drawing up a simple financial forecast will highlight any need to borrow money or look for funding. In week 4 we'll look at straightforward finance, basic accounting and easy budgeting techniques as well as how to raise funds, if this applies.

Friends & Family

In starting and growing your business, will you call on friends and family for advice? If so, refer to this here; mention your board of advisors, your experts-on-call, your support network!

Template 4: Business Plan

Use this template to write your own business plan.

Executive Summary

The Idea

The Market

Customers

Competition

Operations

The CEO

Sourcing

Sales & Marketing

Press

Online

Partners

Systems

Friends & Family

Financials

	Year 1	Year 2
Revenue		
Overheads		
Office rent		
Salary		
Stock		
Technology		
Marketing		
Travel & expenses		
Projected profit		

Week 3

The must dos: registering the company and protecting your brand

As the business comes into being, so does a duty to register the company as a trading entity. There's also the company assets to consider (brand/name/idea) and how to protect them.

Register the Company

When you set up in business, there are a couple of organisations to contact and inform; they are Companies House and HM Revenue & Customs (HMRC). Before registering with either, have a think about the company status that suits you best. There are a number of options:

Self-employed

This status means you are working for yourself; you keep records and accounts of your own activity, and, in acting alone, get to keep all the profits – but are also solely liable for any debts.

If you set up as a self-employed sole trader, you don't need to register with Companies House or take on any of the accounting duties that come with being a limited company, as outlined below.

Partnership

If you'd like to be self-employed but want to work with a friend or colleague, consider a partnership. It means that two or more people share the risks, costs and workload!

Limited company

Limited companies exist in their own right, with the company's finances kept separate from the personal finances of its owners.

• •

The status of your company will affect how much admin you have to do and the kind of financial records to keep and file. Take advice from your accountant or local tax office on which one to choose as much depends on the type of business you will be running.

• •

● ●

TIP: Being social

Should you decide to start a social enterprise, there are additional legal structures to consider, including:

● community interest company

● industrial and provident society

● charitable status.

To find out more about launching a social enterprise or creating a Community Interest Company (CIC) visit:

● **Social Enterprise Coalition**
www.socialenterprise.org.uk

● **CIC regulator**
www.cicregulator.gov.uk

● ●

Companies House

When registering with Companies House, there are two options from which to choose. You can buy a 'ready-made' company from a company formation agent, or 'incorporate' a company yourself by sending documents and a registration fee to Companies House. If you decide to complete registration yourself, download the form from: bit.ly/ezw1S.

Option	Route	Costs
Self-incorporation	Visit the new company registration page of the Companies House website: **bit.ly/dw1xcJ**. Complete form IN01. Post to Companies House with relevant fee.	Standard service fee of £20 (documents processed in eight to ten days). Same-day service fee is £50.
Company formation agent	Visit websites such as the Company Warehouse (**www.thecompanywarehouse.co.uk**), Jordans (**www.jordans.co.uk**), Companies Made Simple (**www.companiesmadesimple.com**), UK Plc (**www.uk-plc.net**).	Prices start at £25/£30 for a standard company.

HM Revenue & Customs

The rules on registering a new business with HM Revenue & Customs are pretty clear cut. You are required to register as soon as you start earning from any business activity. As above, you can choose to register as self-employed, as a partnership, or as a limited company. Each category has its own filing requirements, as outlined below.

Sole trader/self-employed

The calculation of tax and National Insurance owing is done through self-assessment.

You either need to complete form CWF1, or simply call the newly self-employed business helpline. It should be done within three months of undertaking your first piece of self-employed work in order to avoid a fine.

- Form CWF1
  www.hmrc.gov.uk/forms/cwf1.pdf

- Helpline for the newly self-employed
  0845 915 4515

It's not onerous to complete the form and, once registered, you'll be classified as self-employed and sent a self-assessment tax return each year, which you complete, showing your income and expenses from self-employment as well as details of your employment elsewhere (if that applies).

You will be subject to tax and national insurance on any profits you make, but the good news is that any losses incurred can be offset against your employed income (if you have any), which could even result in a tax rebate.

Depending on your turnover and how straightforward your tax affairs are, you may be able to simply fill out the short tax return (SA200). However, this cannot be self-selected, nor is it on the HMRC website or orderable; HMRC will send it to you automatically if they think you qualify, based on information given in the previous year's return. If you have turnover below £68,000, it's likely that you will qualify. As ever, though, it will depend on individual circumstances, and the law (and various criteria it uses) may change!

Deadlines

Self-assessment tax return deadlines are as follows:

- paper tax returns should be received by HMRC by 31 October of tax year ending 5 April.

- online tax returns should be completed by 31 January (giving you an extra three months).

. . . .

TIP: Useful links

- **Leaflet SE1 – 'Thinking of working for yourself?'**
  www.hmrc.gov.uk/leaflets/se1.pdf

- **Helping you understand self-assessment and your tax return**
  www.hmrc.gov.uk/sa

. . . .

Partnership

According to HMRC, a partnership is where:

> "Two or more people set up a business. Each partner is personally responsible for all the business debts, even if the debt was caused by another partner. As partners, each pays income tax on their share of the business profits through self-assessment, as well as National Insurance."

In terms of filing requirements, each partner should complete a partnership supplementary page as part of their individual self-assessment tax return. This is in addition to a partnership return, which has to be submitted by one nominated partner and show each partner's share of profits/losses.

Deadlines

The deadlines for partnership tax returns are as follows:

- paper tax returns should be received by HMRC by 31 October of tax year ending 5 April

- online tax returns should be completed by 31 January (giving you an extra three months).

See page 164 for guidance on how to write a partnership agreement.

CASE STUDY

Name: Oliver Knight, Robert Welch, Alastair Bruton
Business: SmallcarBIGCITY
Started: December 2008

Rob Welch came up with his business idea whilst driving round London in his Classic Mini. He noticed that as he zipped past the most popular sights, more sightseers were turning to look at the Mini than the attractions. It got Rob thinking about how the iconic Mini design was synonymous with the culture and life of London. Tourists shouldn't feel like tourists at all, he thought; they should be immersed in London's culture rather than viewing it at arms' length. And the way to offer this was through running city tours in a Classic Mini!

Things started to happen when Rob met now-fellow-business-partner, Oliver Knight, at a graduate recruitment day, where both were hoping to get hired (and this business was still just a twinkle in his eye). Amongst 50 other hopefuls gunning for potential IT sales roles, Rob and Oliver were dismissed at the first opportunity. The two of them decided to head to the pub! They got talking about their mutual love of London and, as it turned out, Minis. Both were very proud owners.

Rob introduced Oliver to his idea. Next, a business plan was written that established a viable market. And then the business was set up in December 2008. It was the following May (2009) when the two young founders decided to give up their full-time jobs and focus attention on smallcarBIGCITY.

"Soon after that we brought Alastair in to the company," says Oliver. "He is a friend from school who I have known for years. In terms of roles within the company, we are all involved at every stage, with individuals focused on areas we feel the most comfortable and confident in."

"With many small businesses, when you are in the early stages of trading you often find yourself doing a huge variety of tasks. I could be cleaning and fixing a car in the morning and by the afternoon pitching to an international tour operator. Due to the varied nature of each of our roles, communication is vital, not only to ensure we work together as productively as possible, but also to maintain a shared focus on our longer-term development."

The partners find they operate best with a long Monday morning meeting as the focal point for organisation. This allows them to look at the week that's passed and focus on the one ahead, ensuring the team is on top of targets. The next stage of the weekly meet is a sharing of the longer-term vision for the business.

"I believe this weekly catch up and discussion of what we want to achieve beyond the day-to-day running of the business has been essential in maintaining our momentum."

Outside of the Monday meet, communication continues via email, texts and phone calls. This is particularly helpful when it comes to coordinating promotion. The founders are marketing the business through press appearances, working alongside London visitor publications and building relationships with hand-picked hotels that share similarities in terms of iconic design.

"We are also focused on viral marketing: actively using Twitter and Facebook to promote our business and generate interest."

A promotion of which the team is particularly proud revolves around where they managed to hold their second business birthday. The first was in a pub; 2010's was in the Mini showroom on Park Lane!

On the upside of being part of an entrepreneurial partnership, Oliver comments:

"The feeling of sitting down, planning and then executing our strategy is the most gratifying thing in the world. Knowing that through our own thoughts and ideas we have the ability to not only provide ourselves with an income, but also provide a valuable cultural experience in a city that I feel passionate about, in cars that could not be more British, is something that staggers me every day I work on this project."

The team is growing the business and their dream is to expand to other areas of the country – with MGBs in Brighton and Morris Minors in the Cotswolds.

"For the time being we will focus entirely on establishing the business in London, with the possibility of moving the model around the country and perhaps the globe at some stage in the future."

You can't knock this entrepreneurial threesome for their vision and ambition!

- **www.smallcarbigcity.com**
  @smallcarbigcity

Limited company

Limited companies exist in their own right, with the company's finances distinct from the personal finances of the owners. What this means is that the company is liable for any debts, not the individual owners, as is the case if you are self-employed or in a partnership.

In April 2008 it became legal to form and run a limited company with just one person, without the need to involve anyone else (prior to this by law you also needed a company secretary). As noted just now, you can form a new limited company by registering with Companies House (www.companieshouse.gov.uk) or by using a company creation agent.

As well as registering with Companies House, you also need to let HMRC know you are operating as a limited company. You can do this by completing form CT41G.

- Form CT41G
  bit.ly/de4qi9

You will also need to set up and register a PAYE scheme, as you are an employee of the company.

- Register PAYE scheme
  www.hmrc.gov.uk/newemployers

- New employer's helpline
  0845 60 70 143

In terms of filing requirements, you must complete a self-assessment company tax return at the end of the accounting period. The return will show the company's taxable profits and whether any corporation tax is owed and can be filed online at www.hmrc.gov.uk/ct.

The return should also be filed with Companies House to comply with the Companies Act 2006. This can be done free of charge, using the online WebFiling service at Companies House: ewf.companieshouse.gov.uk.

On your returns, you can claim wear-and-tear allowances (capital allowances) on any equipment you buy, and also an element of your expenses for working from home. You can also claim travelling expenses, subsistence and a proportion of your phone calls.

Deadlines

Company tax returns must be filed within 12 months after the end of your company's corporation tax accounting period.

• •

TIP: In good order

Keep records of your business dealings – this will make it much easier to complete tax returns when the time comes. Keep hold of:

- receipts of business-related purchases

- invoices to customers

- bank statements (especially if you don't have a separate account for the business; see page 61 on how to start one)

- utility bills (if you are starting the business from home and using part of the house for business); they can be claimed as a business expense and so reduce your tax bill.

For advice from HMRC on good record keeping, visit:
www.hmrc.gov.uk/startingup/keeprecs.htm

• •

VAT

Whichever tax status you choose, if your business turns over more than £73,000 (in the 2010/11 tax year), or you think your turnover will soon exceed this amount, you should also register for value added tax (VAT).

You can voluntarily register at any time. Being VAT-registered can bring credibility with certain customers, but adding VAT to your invoices may make you more expensive than competitors and you will have to file a VAT return four times a year.

- How and when to register for VAT
  www.hmrc.gov.uk/vat/start/register

Accountant accompaniment

Talk to a qualified accountant about the structure that is best for your business. And consider employing their services to complete your tax returns. Even if your accounts are very simple, it is well worth seeking professional advice, particularly as the rules and regulations can change frequently and without warning.

Find an accountant by visiting:

- ICAEW (Institute of Chartered Accountants in England and Wales)
  www.icaew.com

- List of Sage-accredited professionals
  sage.co.uk/sagedirectory.aspx

- Accountant partners of online software tool, FreeAgentCentral
  www.freeagentcentral.com/partners

- Bitsy, online marketplace of business service providers
  www.bitsythis.com

• •

TIP: Useful links

- **Starting in Business**
  www.hmrc.gov.uk/startingup

- **Tax Help and advice for small business**
  www.businesslink.gov.uk/taxhelp

• •

Business rates

The final form of tax to bear in mind is business rates. If you have applied for planning permission or your Local Authority is aware you are running a business from home, they may try to charge you business rates on the part of the house being used for business purposes, as opposed to council tax. Business rates are different in each area and something that should be agreed with your Local Authority.

- Business Link page on business rates
  bit.ly/grAgTp

See page 65 to determine if you need to contact the Local Authority about planning permission.

Protect the Brand

You have now registered with Companies House and HM Revenue & Customs. Your final consideration should be your intellectual property. You may decide to register a trademark to protect your company name or brand or, if you've come up with a unique invention, a patent. Registering either means that companies can't come along and use your name or invention without your permission.

The four forms of IP

There are four different kinds of intellectual property that you can protect.

1. Patents

These are, essentially, what makes things work. For example, says the Intellectual Property Office (IPO), "what makes a wheel turn or the chemical formula of your favourite fizzy drink."

2. Trade marks

These are "signs (like words and logos) that distinguish goods and services in the marketplace".

3. Designs

What a logo or product looks like: "from the shape of an aeroplane to a fashion item".

4. Copyright

An automatic right that comes into existence for anything written or recorded.

Visit the UK Intellectual Property Office website to carry out searches, register trademarks and read up on all things IP-related.

- Intellectual Property Office
  www.ipo.gov.uk

Week 4

Straightforward finance and easy budgeting techniques

It's become so much easier to start a business on a budget and keep finances in check by keeping overheads low. If you need to raise funds, this section shows you how, as well as offering a simple way to calculate profit through use of a basic spreadsheet.

Straightforward Finance

When planning a business you'll want to be sure earnings are higher than outgoings. Earnings are also referred to as revenue, turnover or income and this should be a greater figure than outgoings, overheads or costs. Let's look at the items that come within each category.

Incoming

Earn from selling your product or service and any associated income opportunities. For example, you set up a business selling unique handmade cushions. From the outset, earn income from:

- Selling 24 x handmade cushions at £25 per cushion = £600 income per week

- Speaking at events to teach others how to make cushions = £150 per event

- Custom requests, e.g. a unique and one-off production = £75 per item

- Developing a blog on the topic of cushions that attracts cushion-istas as readers and paying advertisers as your customers – £priceless!

Outgoings

Here are the costs; some payable at start-up stage and others ongoing:

- Salary – how much do you need to pay yourself? (You will be pleasantly surprised at how thriftily you can live when not commuting.)

- Property – start the business from home and avoid the cost of a pricey second office.

- Raw materials and equipment – what are the materials you need to deliver and promote your finished cushions? And do you need any equipment to make that product; a sewing machine, computer, printer, smartphone or camera?

- Insurance – be insured from the start and choose a policy that covers all your needs.

- Website/promotion materials – we will cover in Weeks 6 and 8 how you can build a home on the web and promote the business on a shoestring of a budget.

Be insured

There are different categories of insurance which you need to know about to secure the policy that's right for you. The main ones are:

- Professional indemnity – relevant to businesses offering services and knowledge and provides protection if you receive a claim alleging a negligent act, error or omission committed by you in the course of the conduct of your professional business.

- Public liability – advisable to have if clients are visiting your home office and/or you are supplying goods to consumers. This will protect you in the event of potential injury to business visitors and/or damages arising from the supply or sale of goods which have caused injury to a third party or their property.

- Business interruption – covers your potential loss of revenue following a material damage loss.

- Employer's liability – only applies when you have employees and offers protection in the event of death or injury to them sustained in the course of their employment.

- Motor insurance – where you own or have use of a motor vehicle on a public road. This is different to standard car insurance, which does not include business use. If you have a vehicle dedicated for business use to carry stock and/or products, you should buy motor insurance or get a business extension on your car insurance policy when using your existing car for business travel.

You are likely to already have a home insurance policy but this will generally not cover business activities carried out at home or business equipment within the home. Speak to your insurance provider and upgrade to a business policy. This is not usually costly but it will ensure you're protected.

● ●

AXA offers a helping hand

AXA Insurance is working hard to make business insurance as easy as possible. Their new website gives plenty of information about the type of cover that's available and that is suitable for start-ups. You can insure your business in minutes online and save money by choosing cover that's tailored to you.

Keep an eye on www.axainsurance.com **or call 0845 366 6481 to talk to AXA's small business insurance experts.**

● ●

Keep records of 'Incoming' and 'Outgoing' in a basic Excel spreadsheet as in the following.

Incoming	
Product sales	£xx
Sponsorship/Advertising	£xx
Other contracts	£xx
Outgoings	
Salary	(£xx)
IT	(£xx)
Office	(£xx)
Raw materials/equipment	(£xx)
Insurance	(£xx)
Marketing & promotion	(£xx)
Other	(£xx)
Profit	**£xx**

See pages 179–180 for a template invoice and how to keep a record of invoices raised and amounts paid.

Starting on a Budget

You probably already have much of what you need to get started in business – i.e. a computer and a mobile phone – so you might not need to buy much more equipment (depending on your business). Here are some tips for keeping costs low.

Start the business from home

Why take on the cost of a second office when the spare room/attic/garden shed will do just as well? Think of the money you'll save: no premises, no commute, no overpriced sandwiches at lunchtime...! The admin side of starting from home is covered on pages 65–6 and in Week 5 we'll show how to turn a home office into the perfect working environment.

Embrace social media

Make the most of free or low-cost technology tools to raise your profile and make sales. Pages 149–154 offer details of the major social media tools and how they can best be used to your benefit, and we'll be getting into that in more detail in Week 9.

Beg, borrow and barter!

When starting out, access all the resources you can. On page 124 Ella Gascoigne tells us how she borrowed a laptop before she'd made sufficient sales to buy one and on page 5 Arianna Cadwallader outlines all the deals she's done to get free event space and discounts on items from sewing machines to cakes!

Work 5 to 9

You can plan the business, register the business and indeed continue to run the business successfully by 'Working 5 to 9' – this is the term I apply to the five-million-plus people who are holding down a day job and building a business at night and weekends.

It's a sensible way to start and grow. You give yourself the time to build confidence and cash flow in the business, and can keep putting money aside until you're ready to go full-time. See the next section for guidance on how and what to tell the boss to make working 5 to 9 as smooth as possible.

• •

TIP: The beauty of barter

Many start-up businesses barter their goods and services, e.g. "I'll produce a sales brochure for you, in exchange for a handmade cushion for my living room." This works well – both parties get what they want. But take heed of the tax implications. Bartering means money doesn't show up in your accounts, but there has been an exchange of goods and services, which implies a taxable activity. The taxman could view bartering as a way to avoid tax. Nevertheless, with so many beneficial arrangements underway, maybe it's time they revised the tax situation?

• •

Working 5 to 9

If you're keeping hold of the day job and growing the business in your spare time, here's what you need to do regarding your current job and boss.

The contract

If you have written terms and conditions of employment they are likely to contain reference to the pursuit of personal business ventures outside your contracted working hours. The clauses to look out for include 'the employee's duties and obligations' and what is commonly known as 'whole time and effort'. These clauses usually require the employee to devote the whole of their time, attention and abilities to the business of the employer.

If your contract contains these or similar clauses, don't despair, as it doesn't necessarily mean you can't pursue your business. Many employment contracts are drafted using standard templates with little consideration to personal circumstance. You know your job better than anyone, so if you don't think your business venture will affect the way you do your job, it probably won't – and your employer will recognise this. Having checked how things stand in the contract, it's time to talk things through with your boss.

The conversation

Treat it as an amicable and informal conversation to gauge your employer's initial reaction.

I asked Patrick Lockton, a qualified lawyer and head of Matrix Law Group (www.matrixlawgroup.com), for his take on the matter and advice on how employees should go about having this conversation:

"When you approach your employer, be prepared to negotiate, be flexible and compromise. If you think it appropriate, make it clear your business venture will in no shape or form affect your ability to do your job or affect your employer's interests. If anything, it will make you a better, more confident and experienced employee and it will not cost your employer a thing."

Patrick goes on to say:

"After having such a conversation, you can do one of two things:

"1. if your employer has not expressed any concerns about your intentions and you have no concerns of your own, disclose your intentions to your employer anyway. Treat it as something you want to do for the sake of clarity and for the record, as opposed to something you want their permission for; or

"2. if your employer has expressed concerns, try and negotiate a package that you are both happy with. Address their concerns, agree some ground rules and get their permission in writing. Give your employer as much helpful information as possible. If you are going to need some time off or to change your hours then this is the time to bring it up.

"Always take written notes so that you don't forget what was said and so you can remind your employer what was agreed."

So long as you're not competing with your employer or breaching their trust, you shouldn't have any problem at all in pursuing your 5 to 9 ambitions. After all, as Patrick says, your employer benefits from all the new skills you're picking up, and it doesn't cost them a penny in training or resources!

CASE STUDY

Name: Kim Scott

Business: Hats my Baby

Started: January 2010

Kim Scott is a shining example of how you can hold down a job and run a business in your spare time. That business is called Hats my Baby and the inspiration for it came whilst Kim was on maternity leave after the birth of her first child.

"In the summer of 2009 we were invited to lots of summer weddings. Finding gorgeous dresses and outfits for our newborn daughter wasn't a problem, but when it came to buying baby hats we were really surprised by the lack of variety on the high street. From there, an idea was born. Before taking maternity leave I was working full-time in the public sector, so setting up the website was a real change in direction for me!"

Before launching the site, Kim announced the launch date using social media such as Twitter and Facebook. She also made the most of small business forums such as Enterprise Nation to spread the word and to pick up useful hints and advice on running a business.

"It was from this early promotion that I secured my first customer and I can still remember how good it felt to receive my very first order. Suddenly all the hard work was worth it."

By concentrating on the niche of baby hats and accessories, Kim can dedicate her time to sourcing products that just aren't available on the high street. This sets the company apart from competitors.

"So far we've concentrated on suppliers within the UK and managed to find some fantastic contacts who have really helped us get on our feet. Generally we've used the internet to source our hats and our aim is to continually add to our range and improve the choice available to customers. We have built the business on a shoe string. But our goal ultimately is to have a baby hat for every season and occasion. We are currently looking at some very gorgeous designs from overseas. Watch this space!"

In promoting the business, Kim has relied heavily on Twitter and Facebook and small business sites. The company recently advertised locally in the press and are delighted to have been approached by a national magazine *Pregnancy and Baby* who featured one of Kim's hats on its shopping pages. Kim and her husband (who is also involved in the business and plays a big part in the design and development of the site) have further ideas in the pipeline for promotion with local photographers. With a part-time job, a young daughter and a young business, Kim has to manage her time well.

"I won't pretend it's easy, as being a mum and working part time is hard enough on its own. But I think what makes it easier is that I believe in the business and I am passionate about it – so any time I spend on it is time well spent. I'm very lucky as my little girl still has a two-hour nap over lunch time, which is the perfect time to catch up on orders. I tend to work in the evening, too, when my daughter has gone to bed. It's all worth it, as I'm building for our future."

Kim dreams of growing the business so it becomes a full-time venture and can justify the cost of a bricks-and-mortar store. In the meantime, and based on her own experience, her advice to anyone wanting to start a business is:

"Do it! Follow your dreams. It really is possible – you just have to believe in yourself. Financially we weren't able to throw a lot of money at the business but we have shown it really is possible to build a business up from next to nothing."

- **www.hatsmybaby.co.uk**
  @hatsmybaby

Funding

Following these steps and Working 5 to 9 will help your budgeting, but if you think you'll need funding all the same, here are a few places to look.

Friends and family

Friends and family are people you can trust – and asking them for money hopefully won't come with strings attached! Do consider having a written agreement, though, that covers the amount borrowed and a payback schedule.

The bank

High street banks are pretty eager to attract small business owners. Make the most of their enthusiasm and ask to speak to a small business advisor at your local branch. Take a copy of your business plan with you and be prepared to talk through it.

Credit cards

Many a business has been started with help from a flexible friend! Shop for the best rates. It's a competitive market and the credit card companies are keen for your business. Be on time with repayments (to avoid penalty interest charges) and aim to pay back the credit as soon as you can and as sales start coming in. This route is suggested based on start-up costs being small and the ability to pay back at speed so avoiding monthly repayments at high interest rates.

- -

TIP: A clear division

Open a bank account early on so you don't mix up your business and personal finances, which may complicate record keeping. To open a bank account you'll need to provide details of your business, a business plan and a certificate of incorporation for limited companies. Find out more about bank account opening requirements on the Business Link website.

- **bit.ly/hh3war**

- -

Grants

There are grants available from a number of sources, including the government, European Union, local authorities and some charitable organisations, such as the Prince's Trust.

Find out more about grants and other help that may be available to you at:

- Business Link
  www.businesslink.gov.uk

- National Federation of Enterprise Agencies (with links to your local enterprise agency)
  www.nfea.com

- The Prince's Trust (funds available to help young people start a business)
  www.princes-trust.org.uk

- PRIME (offers a Zopa-PRIME Olderpreneur Loan)
  www.primebusinessclub.com

- J4b Grants (grants, loans and venture capital)
  www.j4bgrants.co.uk

Crowd funding

Crowd funding is a relatively recent development that involves sourcing funds from a group of others, with each lending a proportion of the total you wish to borrow. Check out www.zopa.com where you can secure a loan from people willing to lend.

• •

TIP: Helping hand from Enterprise Nation

At Enterprise Nation we're looking into the possibility of being able to make small start up loans to support business ideas that need a bit of cash to get going. Register for the e-news at www.enterprisenation.com to be the first to know about developments.

• •

Investors

Angel investors and venture capitalists can help raise large amounts of start-up funding or development capital for businesses looking to grow. It might be an idea to consider this route further down the line. It doesn't have to be a gruesome experience, though (a la *Dragons' Den*) as there are plenty of funds and investors out there who are eager to part with their money and back good ideas. Unlike banks, investors will be looking for equity, i.e. part ownership in your business in return for the funds.

- Angels Den
  www.angelsden.co.uk

- Funding Circle
  www.fundingcircle.com

- British Business Angels Association
  www.bbaa.org.uk

Week 5

It's your office! Tech tips and how to create the perfect work environment

One of the great benefits of being your own boss is the ability to work where and how you like, whilst wearing what you like! Create an environment to suit and equip your office with the technology, gadgets and accessories that will deliver a productive end result.

Household Admin

Over 60% of businesses are started from home on account of the low costs and lack of commute. When you start and grow your business from home, you may have a few questions about whom you need to inform. Here are the answers!

Q: Do I need planning permission?

A: You'll need planning permission to base the business at home if you answer 'yes' to any of these questions:

- will your home no longer be used mainly as a private residence?

- will your business result in a marked rise in traffic or people calling?

- will your business involve any activities that are unusual in a residential area?

- will your business disturb the neighbours at unreasonable hours or create other forms of nuisance such as noise or smells?

If your house is pretty much going to remain a house, with your business quietly accommodated within it, then permission shouldn't be required. If you're unsure, contact your local council to seek their views.

- www.planningportal.gov.uk

Q: Do I need to tell the local authority I'm working from home?

A: This depends on whether you pass the planning test. If you need planning permission, you'll have to inform your local authority. If you don't, then the only benefit of telling them is that they'll charge you business rates (rather than council tax) on the part of the house being used for business purposes – not really much of an incentive! Business rates are different in each area and something that should be agreed with your local authority.

- Business Rates information on Business Link website
  bit.ly/grAgTp

Q: Do I need to tell the landlord?

A: Yes, it's best to let them know that you will be working from home. The good news is that the coalition government announced on 1 November 2010 that social landlords should review any contracts prohibiting people from running a business from home.

Q: Do I need to inform my mortgage provider?

A: Yes, it's best to let them know – even though it shouldn't mean any change in the mortgage repayment.

Q: What about my insurance provider? Do they need to know?

A: Yes, do inform your insurance company. Tell them about the equipment and stock you have at home. An upgrade from domestic to a business policy is not usually expensive so don't be put off in making this call. Your insurance provider is likely to recommend that you also take out public liability insurance in case anyone who comes to visit suffers an injury in or around your home office. See page 54 for details of the type of insurance you may need.

Q: Do I need protection for when customers and contacts come to visit?

A: Yes, carry out a health and safety check, which is easy to do by following the steps set out by the Health and Safety Executive in their *Homeworking* guide (pdf available at bit.ly/aGDc8N).

- Health and Safety Executive
  www.hse.gov.uk

Q: Should I tell the neighbours?

A: Yes. See pages 68–9 for more advice!

Here is an admin template so you can check all this is in order.

Template 5: Admin Checklist

Task	Completed?
Informed the council (if required)	
Updated insurance policy	
Done health and safety check	
Informed mortgage provider	
Told the neighbours	
Registered company with Companies House (Week 3)	
Registered company with HMRC (Week 3)	
Any other business	

If running a business from home

Task	Completed?
Informed Local Authority (only relevant if planning permission is required)	
Informed mortgage provider	
Checked insurance provision	
Contacted Health and Safety re inspection of kitchen (if using domestic kitchen for commercial catering)	
Carried out health and safety check	
Told the neighbours	

Everyone needs good neighbours

When working from home, it's worth keeping your neighbours sweet and firmly on side. You don't want them getting annoyed by any deliveries or unusual distractions.

- Explain to your neighbours that you are running a business from home and that it shouldn't cause them any disturbance. (If it will cause them disturbance, see above: you'll need planning permission!)

- Keep your promise and try to keep disruptions to a minimum. Avoid big heavy deliveries at anti-social hours and streams of client traffic clogging up the roads.

- If the business reaches a major milestone, maybe host a party for your neighbours. A friend of mine said his neighbours were more than happy to 'be on the telly' when his home business appeared on a Sky News live broadcast from his home office!

- Make friends with other homeworkers in your neighbourhood, so you can demonstrate together that the way you work is beneficial to the economy of the area and its safety, as for example you can keep an eye on your neighbours' houses during the day.

- If you know of a time when there'll be an unusual amount of activity in your home office, let your neighbours know in advance and perhaps send a bottle of wine to thank them for their cooperation.

TIP: The benefits of a home-based business

There are benefits to the business, and to your life, in starting a business from home.

Work benefits	Life benefits
The 60-second commute!	Feeling happier, healthier and more balanced, and enjoying the benefits this brings to your relationships
Getting more done, without distractions	Wearing what you like
The financial savings	Dancing in the office!
Being able to give your clients personal service and a homely welcome when they visit the office	Being a friend to the environment
Adding to the property value of your home (research carried out on my website showed that homes with offices sell for an average £25,000 more than homes without offices)	Going shopping when there are no queues

Setting Up With IT

Building the right IT system for your business needn't mean starting from scratch or spending lots of money. Once your business grows you can upgrade your technology as and when funds become available. To start with, there are affordable, even free, solutions that can get you up and running in no time at all. Chances are that you have some of them already!

So, let's take a look at what you might already have and what you might need to buy. And we'll separate them by hardware and software.

Hardware

Hardware is the physical components of your IT system. At a basic level, it includes things like your keyboard and mouse, but can extend to include new devices and gadgets that we'll look at in a moment. First, let's list the basic components of a start-up IT system.

Computer

When starting out, using your home's shared computer will be just fine. Bear in mind, however, that in the first few months of starting your business you may find yourself working more hours than usual, trying to get it all set up – so prepare cohabiting friends and family for the possibility of reduced access!

Also, when your business grows, the data you accumulate – information on your customers, clients and contacts, including financial details – will become more and more valuable. You might then think twice about sharing your computer with the rest of the family.

For that reason, and the flexibility you'll have in deciding when and where you can work, I'd recommend looking into buying a separate laptop computer if you don't have one already. There was a time when doing so was much more expensive than buying a desktop computer, but in recent years the prices have almost levelled off. Budget laptops start at around £300, but when buying computers it's important to buy the best that you can afford. It'll help you prepare for the future, when new software is released with new demands on your hardware; it'll help you run more programs at once and hold more data, as your business grows; and it'll take the sting out of your purchase when prices start to drop in a few months time!

If you've decided to buy a new computer, here are the things to look out for:

Processor
The processor is the speed of your computer. The higher the number, the faster your computer can run.

Memory
More memory (RAM) increases overall performance and enables your computer to run more programs at once. Try and buy a computer with as much RAM as you can afford. A common frustration amongst computer users is how long it can take to launch programs and switch between them. More RAM equals less waiting.

Hard drive
The hard drive gives you space for all your data and programs. This can easily be expanded with a second, external hard drive, but you'll be surprised at how quickly it will fill up, especially if you're also storing personal data, like music and photos, on your computer.

Display (for desktops)
You'll be hard pressed to find a computer that comes with a big, CRT display nowadays. Most are sold with slim, flat-screen monitors. If you don't have one already, consider upgrading. You'll save lots of space in your office and, if you get a bigger screen with a higher resolution, you could get more work done, as you'll have more virtual workspace to open programs and documents.

Standard features
You should expect to find an optical drive, for 'burning' CDs and DVDs, and wireless connectivity, so you can get on the internet wherever you are, with all new computer purchases.

Peripherals

Peripherals are devices that can be used with your computer but are not an integral part of it. I don't want to call them 'accessories', because some of the peripherals I use, I couldn't live without!

Multifunction printer
Even though I find myself using it less these days, with most information passed around electronically, I still think it's too early to pronounce the printer dead, especially if you use a multifunction printer like I do.

It's a real space-saver – imagine keeping a printer, scanner, photocopier and fax machine in one office! You'd have no room to do any work. Mine sits neatly on my desk and is particularly handy when I want to email sketches to my designer. He uses his to archive printed documents. When he receives important letters, for example, he scans them into his computer and recycles the hard copy! We're both on our way to paperless home offices.

External hard drive

I've already mentioned external hard drives. They're great for extending the storage capacity of your computer – so you can keep more data and programs – but they're especially useful for backing up the entirety of your machine. This is a vital process which you should do regularly – imagine the implications if your computer crashed and wouldn't reboot; or if something worse happened. Look for ones with USB 2.0 connections or, if you're using a Mac, a relevant FireWire connection.

They're easy to set up – you just plug them in and they show up in your operating system as another drive. You can then just drag and drop important folders or use special software that automates the process for you. Macs have this software built-in; as do the latest PCs. If not, try SuperDuper! for the Mac and True Image for the PC.

- SuperDuper!
  www.shirt-pocket.com/SuperDuper

- True Image
  www.acronis.com

Webcam

A webcam enables you to video chat with clients and contacts and is useful when you need to have a 'face to face' meeting but can't get away. Most Macs have webcams built into their screen; for PC webcams try Logitech.

- Logitech
  www.logitech.com

Speakers

Liberated in being your own boss and working in your own office, listen to your favourite music whenever you like! If you're a music fan treat yourself, and your iTunes library, to a good pair of speakers. Some are designed to be a treat for the eyes as well as the ears. My favourite set is made by a company called JBL.

- JBL Home Audio
  www.jbl.com

Keyboard and mouse

Years ago, mice used to work with a ball inside that would be pushed around your desk on a mouse pad. But nowadays, there's a new technology – optical – which means no moving parts and no way for dust to get inside and interfere with the sensors. If you don't have one already, you should get one!

Again, Logitech do a nice range. They also have some good keyboards, some of which are ergonomically designed to prevent repetitive strain injury (RSI) and wireless to cut down on clutter. Have a look around for a keyboard and mouse set and save money.

- Logitech
  www.logitech.com

VoIP phones

You can make serious savings on your phone bill by using a VoIP phone. VoIP stands for 'voice over internet protocol' and it basically means making calls over the internet rather than by using your phone line. As such, it's a much cheaper way of making calls (it's sometimes free). And it's the easiest way to set up a second line. The VoIP phone I use is made by a company called IPEVO, who make handsets in black or white to go with your Mac or PC.

- IPEVO
  www.ipevo.com

Software

Software consists of the programs and operating system that your computer uses. Again, you'll be using many of them already in your everyday life, so there's no need to splash out when setting up your business. Once it grows you can upgrade to more advanced versions. To start, here are the basics. Later we'll look at software (much of it free or very affordable) for when your business is up and running. See pages 160 and 177.

Office software

By far, the industry standard in office software, for both Mac and PC computers, is Microsoft Office, which includes a word processor as well as presentation and spreadsheet program.

- Microsoft Office for small business
  office.microsoft.com/en-gb/small-business

If you're trying to bootstrap, try this free alternative:

- OpenOffice.org
  www.openoffice.org

It's called OpenOffice and does pretty much everything that Microsoft Office can do, plus it can open and save Microsoft Office files too. It does take some getting used to, but the support is pretty good. It's worth a try!

• •

TIP: Getting connected

You'll need broadband right from the start: during your research, while you're setting up your business, through to when it grows and takes over the world!

Your two main options are ADSL broadband, which is offered by companies like BT and Sky, and cable broadband from Virgin Media. The biggest difference is that ADSL requires a phone line, while cable broadband does not.

The advantage of cable broadband is that if you don't have a landline phone, and always use your mobile, you can save money by not having to pay line rental on your phone as well as on your internet connection. It's often faster, too, but you'll need to check whether it's available in your area. ADSL broadband is more commonplace and there are lots of companies offering it. As always, read the fine print before you sign anything. Here are some things to look out for:

Price
Some broadband prices seem really cheap but often the prices advertised are for the first few months of an 18-month contract, so make sure you know what you're getting into before you sign anything.

Usage
Some broadband companies will set restrictions on the amount of data you can download in a month and sometimes even charge you extra if you go over your agreed limit. These limits rarely affect most users, but if your business is the kind that needs to send and receive lots of information, look for deals with generous monthly download allowances. Or, better still, unlimited downloads.

Customer support

If you're installing broadband for the first time, you might need some help setting up and also, once you're up and running, knowing what to do when your connection suddenly drops. For these sorts of queries it's handy to have good customer support, so check to see what's on offer and, crucially, how much it would cost to call for help.

Network

Setting up a network used to be the work of professionals and, I suppose, in big companies it still is. But setting one up for your home by yourself is much easier these days.

Your internet service provider may have already provided you with a router – a device that allows you to share your internet connection with other computers in your home. And many are now giving out wireless routers for free, so you can connect to the internet all around the house – and even in the garden!

There are two types of wireless router: one for ADSL internet service providers, like Sky and BT, and another for cable internet, like Virgin Media. Check with your internet service provider to find out which is the best router for your type of connection.

I didn't get a free wireless router with my provider, but a friend recommended one that I can to you too. It's from a company called Netgear, and it looks quite nice too!

- Netgear
  www.netgear.co.uk

Web browser

All computers come with web browsers pre-installed. It's the program that allows you to see web pages on the internet. PCs typically use a browser called Internet Explorer, and Macs a program called Safari.

Both do a good job, but there's a browser I use that's just as good. It's called Chrome and it's made by the people at Google. It's fast, secure and customisable, so you can add features that will help you do your work and manage your lifestyle. These include features like URL shortening, comparison shopping and changing the way your browser looks. It's a free, small download that won't take up much storage and it works on Macs and PCs.

- Google Chrome
  www.google.com/chrome

Email

Again, computers come with email software preinstalled. On PCs the software is called Outlook Express (or on newer PCs Windows Mail) and on Macs it's just called Mail. If you've got Microsoft Office you might use Outlook (or Entourage, as it's called in the Mac version), which is Outlook Express's big sister. It includes calendar and address book features.

POP mail vs. web mail

There are two kinds of email – POP and IMAP. Non-web-based email that you usually use in a program like Outlook or Apple's Mail is called POP mail and it works by downloading messages from a server onto your computer. IMAP is becoming more popular, as it is more convenient for those who use email on several devices, like a laptop, a home computer or a smartphone. You can get POP on those things too, but you end up with copies of messages, which can be confusing. IMAP does a better job of keeping everything in sync, so your inbox looks the same, wherever you are.

Web mail is accessed through a web browser, like Google Chrome or Internet Explorer. However, whilst that's very handy and such web mail is widely provided for free through services like Microsoft's Hotmail or Google's Gmail, it is perhaps less professional-sounding than POP mail. POP mail can be addressed at your domain (for example emma@enterprisenation.com). My Hotmail address, on the other hand, is enterprisenation@hotmail.co.uk, which doesn't look quite as good!

But there is a solution that Google provides. It's called Google Apps and it allows you to use all of its web-based features, like email, calendar and instant messaging *at your own address*. It's especially good for small businesses and organisations – and it's free! You just need to own your own domain, like I do: www.enterprisenation.com.

- Google Apps
  www.google.com/a

Instant messaging and VoIP

A great way to stay in touch with friends and colleagues is by instant messaging (IM), which allows you to exchange typed messages over the internet in real-time.

So it's not like email, where there's typically a delay in the response. Instant messaging is more like chatting. And if you work from home, it instils an office-like atmosphere in your very own home office.

Lots of instant messaging programs also allow you to make video and voice calls. The program I use is Skype and it integrates text, voice and video chat. It allows me to make free calls to other Skype users and to landline or mobile phones for a small fee, which is deducted from pay-as-you-go style 'Skype credit'.

You can even assign a landline-sounding phone number to your Skype account, so you can receive calls at your computer, using a VoIP handset (see page 73), or divert calls to your mobile when you're out and about. It's worth trying it out before you spend money installing a second line.

- Skype
  www.skype.com

TIP: Superfast broadband

BT is investing over £2 billion to deliver superfast fibre broadband to two-thirds of UK homes by the end of 2015. If you live in an area with an activated exchange, new speeds will power your business and enable you to work faster online and download rich digital media in no time. Find out if fibre is coming to your home by visiting www.bt.com/superfastbroadband.

Support

If you're in need of assistance with anything from hardware set-up to software installation, then call in the help of a local IT expert. You may know a neighbour who's a dab hand at technology. If not, you can check out one of a growing number of companies who send a 'geek' direct to your door, or visit our site Bitsy and click on the 'IT web and software' category to gain access to a whole range of friendly technical experts.

- Geeks-on-Wheels
  www.geeks-on-wheels.com

- The TechGuys
  www.thetechguys.com

- Geek Squad
  www.geeksquad.co.uk

- Tech Tuesday on Bitsy
  bitsythis.com/groups/tech-tuesday

Template 6: Tech Checklist

Follow this tech checklist to ensure systems continue to run smoothly.

Task	Completed?
Have you restarted your computer recently?	
Have you updated your software via Windows or Mac Software Update?	
Is your anti-virus software up-to-date?	
Have you backed up recently (and do so regularly)?	
Do you have a sufficiently cryptic password that you change regularly?	
Any other business	

Tech support

Check out EasyTech, a range of Staples products that will help you set up your computer and keep it working like new.
www.staples.co.uk/easytech

Creating the perfect work environment

Create the perfect work environment for you and your business and follow this checklist to ensure you're working profitably and productively.

Find dedicated space

If the business is based at home, try to create an area in the house that functions as your dedicated workspace. That way you can mentally adjust yourself to be in business mode when in that space. It helps you to know when you should be working and when you should be taking a break.

It will also help make it clear to friends and family that when you're in your home office, you're working. And when the door's closed, it means, 'I'm busy. Please don't disturb'.

This dedicated space could be a spare room, in the attic, under the stairs or even the garden shed. For garden office dwellers, one blog you will like is Shedworking (**www.shedworking.co.uk**).

A light touch

Lots of light is good for your mood and work pace but avoid too much task-light shining on the computer monitor. As for colours on the walls, go for light shades as they will make the space look bigger, and consider mirrors to bounce light around.

Invest in a good desk and chair

Depending on the nature of your business, you could be spending a good few hours each day at the desk and in your chair, so be sure they're both sturdy and comfortable! Buy a chair that's designed for computer use – and try it out first. Sitting in an awkward position can put your body under stress, so make sure you can adjust the chair's height and angle to suit you. Ideally, your feet should be flat on the floor and your back straight. Getting this right will make working from home so much more comfortable!

Get a good, sturdy desk that can accommodate your computer, monitor, keyboard and mouse. The top of your monitor should be at eye level and the monitor itself about an arm's length away from you.

Office furnishings

Creating the right setting for a business is important. Staples stores have a wide selection of desks, chairs, desk tidies and files that will suit all work spaces, no matter how big or small.

Double-up

Invest in storage boxes and turn your wardrobes into filing cabinets! Or buy big boxes, label them well and then find a place to hide them away; maybe doubling up as a chair for visitors.

* * *

A spring clean

Wondering what to do with all the stuff in the room that you want to use as your home office? Take space with a company like Access Storage and have your goods accessible but out of the way, or give them up to a recycling company such as Green Works, so that your unwanted items can go to a home that does want them!

- Access Self Storage
  www.accessstorage.com

- Green Works
  www.green-works.co.uk

* * *

Have a vision

Put a vision board up on the wall and on it stick pictures that represent your personal and business ambitions; places you want to visit, targets for the company, and people with whom you enjoy spending time. Glance at it each day to remind yourself of everything you're working for and towards.

Office vision board

Keeping track of what you're doing and where you're heading is fundamental. Staples stores stock white boards in all shapes and sizes, complete with dry-wipe pens in a variety of colours. All you have to do is map out the future.

Week 6

Building a home on the web

You have the tools and connection to get online. The first thing to do is build a presence through a blog, website or store. Not only is a website your window to the world and home on the web, it has become an essential requirement for any new business.

Home on the Web, Window to the World

Your site is a powerful marketing tool and a way to make money. Having the right technology and knowledge allows you to build, develop and maintain your site. And you can do it all in-house.

Let's look at the three main ways to develop a professional looking online presence.

1. Blogging

Blogging is a website or part of a website that's regularly updated by an individual or a group of 'bloggers'. There are blogs on any number of topics and the fact that anyone can start blogging for free makes the medium diverse and exciting.

It's an easy way to get online, as you write posts on your topic of choice, upload images and video and become the go-to place for customers looking for your advice/tips/services/products. Search engines love blogs and the more you write, the higher up the search-engine ranks you will go. Writing regularly is likely to lead to a loyal readership and it's an effective way to communicate your news with existing and potential customers. Readers can add their comments to your entries if you allow them and you can use your blog to answer questions and establish yourself as an expert in your field.

It's free and easy to get started. Try one of the services below.

- Blogger
  www.blogger.com

- TypePad
  www.typepad.com

- WordPress
  www.wordpress.com

See pages 112–5 for details on how to make money from your blog.

2. Your own website

Create a home on the web through having your own website that you have built to your own requirements or by investing in a template website. Let's look at both options.

DIY

You have decided to build your own site or have a developer take care of it for you.

The first thing to do is buy a domain, i.e. a URL. A domain makes up a part of your website and email address. So, for example, the domain name I own is enterprisenation.com. My website address is www.enterprisenation.com and my email address is emma@enterprisenation.com. Both use the enterprisenation.com domain name.

A domain isn't only your address on the web it's also a big part of your brand on the internet so think carefully when choosing one – although your options will be increasingly limited, since so many combinations have already been snapped up!

There are domain registration companies whose websites allow you to check for available domain names and often suggest available alternatives. Here are three that I've come across.

- 1&1
  www.1and1.co.uk

- 123-reg
  www.123-reg.co.uk

- Easily.co.uk
  www.easily.co.uk

Registering a domain name doesn't give you a website, just an address for it (and an email address). Think of it like reserving a car parking space. You've got the space, now you need to buy the car!

A hosting company will sort you out with the web space to host your website. This is measured in megabytes and gigabytes, just like the information on your computer. You upload the files that make up a website – pictures and pages – to this space, so that the rest of the world can see them.

In terms of how much web space you will need, basic hosting packages offer about 250MB of web space, but anything over 1 or 2GB is more sensible and it will also allow you to handle more traffic on your website as it grows more popular.

With a domain name and web space, potential customers should be able to type your website address into their browser and find out all about your business – just as soon as you've built your site. Finding a hosting company shouldn't be hard. Most domain registration companies, including those mentioned above, offer web space as a package and vice versa.

• •

TIP: A website for free

In 2010, the 'Getting British Business Online' (GBBO) project was launched by Google and offered free websites to 100,000 businesses. GBBO is growing in 2011 by continuing to offer free websites and helping online businesses expand. Visit www.gbbo.co.uk and sign up for your own free website.

• •

When it comes to hiring a designer, have a think about what you'd like your website to do for your business. The easiest way to start is to think of your website as a brochure, but remember to include the following pages at the very least.

Basic pages to include

- About us

- News

- Products or services

- FAQs (Frequently Asked Questions)

- Contact us

Choose a designer who has carried out work you like the look of and for companies in a similar kind of sector to your own. That way, the designer will understand what site you're after – and what your kind of visitor will be looking for, as well as how they like to browse and buy. Check out Bitsy (www.bitsythis.com) or similar sites to find the right web designer for you.

See pages 106–7 for details on how to integrate PayPal payments into your site and turn site content into commerce.

How to brief a web designer/developer

Here is Emily Hewett's (www.birdsontheblog.co.uk) advice on how best to brief a web designer/developer:

When working with a designer you need to have a coherent brief for them to follow. Here are my hints and tips to help you be clear in your mind what it is you want so you can communicate this to your designer and use the brief as a point of reference throughout the project.

Who are you? – even if the designer has worked with your organisation previously, always give them a short summary of your company; who you are and what you do. This will help refresh their memory and tune in to your particular industry sector. You will also need to tell them about your market and how you fit in to the larger scheme of things, for example who your competitors are both locally and nationally.

What do you want to achieve? – you need to detail the purpose, for example are you wanting to capture data, generate sales, increase footfall, etc.

Who are you talking to? – outline a profile of who your customer is. The designer will need to know whether they are targeting females, males or both, what is the age group of the audience, what is their average income and what's their location.

What tone are you using? – deciding on how you speak to your audience is important. You may be writing the copy yourself or you may have a copywriter to do this for you. In this section of the brief tell the designer if it's a laidback chatty tone or a formal, informative tone. The tone of the copy will affect the design and these two elements need to gel to produce a successful end product.

What are your likes and dislikes? – provide examples to the designer wherever possible of what you like or don't like online. It might be a certain colour palette or illustration style or it could be a format. Any of these things help the designer get into your head and understand what it is that you require, making for a better working relationship.

Are there any mandatory elements? – tell the designer if there are any mandatory fonts, colours, logos, legal text, images, etc. so that they can make sure they are producing something on brand that adheres to your corporate image.

What's your budget? – this doesn't need to be set in stone and a good designer won't take a large budget and fit a job to it, they should find the most cost-effective way of producing exactly what you want, but if you have a small budget the designer will have to make decisions based on what they can realistically achieve in that price bracket.

When do you want it? – make the designer aware of your ultimate deadline that needs to be achieved.

Have you covered everything? – show the brief to a colleague or friend to see if they understand the content and once happy with the brief, send or talk it through with your designer and invite questions so they are aware you are approachable and that you are both working from the same list of requirements.

Doing this not only creates a good bond between you and your designer, it also helps you clarify what you really want from your website.

Emily Hewett, Birds on the Blog
www.birdsontheblog.co.uk

Template site

If DIY feels and sounds too much like hard work, there are a good number of companies offering template websites that come with domain registration, hosting, e-commerce and a basic level of design as part of the package.

There are a number of template site providers offering websites that can be set up today and trading by tomorrow.

● ●

TIP: Take care of the Ts and Cs

When building your site, include some basic terms and conditions. These will cover information about the site content and your policy on data privacy. View sample terms & conditions on the Business Link website: bit.ly/csYSTz

● ●

Product	Price	Features
Actinic www.actinic.co.uk	Actinic Express £1 set-up fee and £18 per month thereafter. Free 30-day trial on offer.	Company has been established in the UK since 1996 and has built a solid reputation.
Create www.create.net	Packages start from £2.99 per month. 30-day free trial available.	Set up your site in minutes and benefit from email support plus online forums.
CubeCart www.cubecart.com	From free to £110, depending on the features required (**cubecart.com/ features**)	E-commerce shopping cart used by more than one million store owners – so they must be doing something right! Free 30-day trial on offer.
Mr Site www.mrsite.com	3 packages: £19.99 Beginner £34.99 Standard £99.99 Professional	Used by a good number of home businesses and 5 to 9'ers, you can buy the product in boxed or email format. Helpful tips on how to start via the site.
osCommerce www.oscommerce.com	Free	An open source solution with, to date, over 5,800 add-ons available for free to customise your store and increase sales.
Powa www.powa.com	2 packages: £9.99 per month for content-only site £49.99 per month for e-commerce site	Based on technology developed by venda.com which powers websites for large retailers such as Monsoon and Jimmy Choo, Powa.com makes the same features available for small business at a smaller price. Easy to use and customise.

Prices correct at time of publication.

These tips are offered by Joanna Tall, founder of OffToSeeMyLawyer.com.

1. Display terms of use

Think of your website like a board game you are about to play with your visitors. They arrive and are ready to play and you need to state the rules or else it will be chaos! So, for example, state what they can and cannot do – e.g. may they copy your materials? May they rely on the information you provide without double-checking with you or elsewhere? What liability are you prepared to accept? Provide a link to your terms of use, ideally on every page of your website or under a 'Legals' section.

2. Display your privacy policy

Most websites collect personal data of their visitors either by getting them to register on the site or sign up for a newsletter. By law you must tell visitors what you will be doing with this data and the best way to do this is to set out the information in a so-called privacy policy. Again, a link to it on every page is best. More complex rules apply if you plan to collect sensitive information or information from children, or want to pass the information to third parties; for this you should consult a lawyer. Additionally, you are likely to need to register as a data processor under the Data Protection Act. Simply go to **www.ico.gov.uk** for more information.

3. If selling goods or services online, display your terms of sale

Just as with the board game example, you need rules for selling your goods or services. Most importantly, you need to get your visitors to acknowledge that they accept them. So ideally get them to tick a box stating that they accept them before they proceed to check out. You also need to draw their attention to their rights under the Distance Selling Regulations, e.g. cancellation rights amongst others.

See page 108 for details of the Distance Selling Regulations.

4. Protect your copyright in the website content

Although you automatically own the copyright in the content that you create, best practice is to remind your visitors! Say, for example: "Copyright 2011 Lawyers R Great Ltd" and if your logo or name is trademarked, broadcast the fact! After all, you will have spent a lot of money in getting it that far and it will enhance your brand in the market.

5. State who you are!

By law you need to state a full postal address and contact number and if you are a limited company, the company's registered address, number and country of registration. This also applies to your emails, so add these details to your signature.

Joanna Tall is founder of www.offtoseemylawyer.com, *where most terms and conditions can be bought from the 'oven ready' document shop.*

3. A presence on other sites

Maybe you'd prefer to start raising your profile and making sales via other platform sites, as opposed to your own. Whether you are selling boutique crafts or business concepts, there are a number of options.

The upside is that these sites attract customers on your behalf, and some of them attract customers from all over the world. Here are five web platforms that enable you to sell.

eBay

eBay has grown to become the largest shopping mall on the web. In 2010 there were 160,000 registered businesses trading on the site in the UK, generating sales of £1.6 billion a year. The good thing is, having a store on eBay means you are opened up to an international audience and many potential customers!

- www.eBay.co.uk

TIP: eBay advice

eBay expert, Dan Wilson, offers 5 tips on how to make the most of the mega marketplace known as eBay:

1. Start small
Go slow until you've found your way. Start with a few, easy-to-post items and learn about eBay before boosting your range and prices. Don't stake too much on your first eBay bet.

2. Sell like you mean it
The eBay marketplace is competitive and you'll lose out unless you have top-notch listings. Craft fabulous item titles, make impeccable pictures and write descriptions that tempt buyers. Be truthful and honest and look professional from the start.

3. Be quick off the mark

Buyers have come to expect great service. Dispatch orders quickly — preferably within 24 hours of payment — and well packed, and make sure you reply to emails and other communications swiftly, too. The quality and speed of your replies and dispatches has an impact on customer feedback.

4. Put a lid on postal costs

Understand postage and packaging costs and make sure you factor it in to your costs where necessary.

5. Loyalty means profit

When you're building your eBay business, encouraging repeat buyers is important. Once a buyer trusts you as an online seller, they're likely to keep coming back. Offer discounts and incentives with every dispatch and cross-market complementary products.

Dan Wilson is an eBay expert and author of Make Serious Money on eBay UK, www.wilsondan.co.uk

Bitsy

Whether you're a web designer, an accountant or marketer, Bitsy connects your business services with business buyers. We refer to it as the friendliest business-to-business marketplace on the web. You can list your business in the Bitsy directory from just £5 per month. It's supported by a business blog, with tips and advice on sales and marketing, IT efficiency, productivity and motivation, and a community for all the help and support you need to start and grow your business.

- www.bitsythis.com
  @BitsyTalk

Alibaba.com

Having a presence on this site enables you to buy and sell and source supplies with companies from across the globe. The site has visitors from 240 countries and regions, with over 660,000 registered users in the UK. Through the site you can locate suppliers or make sales of your finished product direct to customers. Alibaba.com is a champion of international trade; carrying out research on the topic, providing a platform for traders to interact, and promoting overseas sales as a form of business that is wholly viable, regardless of company size.

- www.alibaba.com
  @AlibabaTalk_UK

Amazon Marketplace

You may be used to buying from Amazon, but have you considered the site as a platform from which to sell? Have your products appear before millions of customers all around the world by signing up to Amazon Marketplace. It offers two sales options: a package for casual sellers who expect to sell less than 35 items a month (a fixed fee per sale plus a referral fee), and for more seasoned sellers there is the 'sell a lot' package, which has a monthly charge plus a referral fee for unlimited sales that do not have to be in the Amazon catalogue.

- www.amazon.co.uk/marketplace

Etsy.com

With its tag line 'Your place to buy and sell all things handmade' this is still the mother of all craft sites. Since the company launched in June 2005, more than 400,000 sellers from around the world have opened up Etsy shops and buyers of Etsy-listed products span more than 150 countries. To start selling on Etsy you need to register for an account (this requires a credit card and valid email address for verification purposes) and then it costs 20 cents to list an item for four months. When your item sells, you pay a 3.5% transaction fee. For anyone who makes handmade items, the power of this global platform cannot be denied.

- www.etsy.com
  @etsy

TIP: Sales site for students

If you're a student with creative skills, Concept Cupboard (www.conceptcupboard.com) will appeal because it connects businesses with creative students and graduates. Projects are profiled on the site along with a budget and you pitch to do the job. Selling made simple!

See below for a listing of other sites on which you can sell all things handmade.

Top sites for selling

Site	Listing fee	Commission	Other features/information
Etsy.com	20 cents per item	3.5%	
CraftNation.com	None	None	Monthly packages (£4.99/£9.99) for listing over 5 products
Folksy.com	20p per item	5%	
Alllthingsoriginal.com	None	Undisclosed	Free to join and list but through a selection process. A commission is taken on each sale – confirmed on application
DaWanda.com	None	5%	Listing fee may be introduced in the future
Notonthehighstreet.com	Undisclosed	Undisclosed	The company does not disclose listing fees and commission as charges are tailor made for each company
DreamAid.com	None	10%	Option for a percentage of sales price to go to DreamAid charity
MISI.co.uk	20p per item	3%	
Artfire.com	None	None	$12 per month to upgrade account
Coriandr.com	20p per item	2.5%	Can request free promotion flyers

Prices correct at time of publication.

Site	Listing fee	Commission	Other features/information
Giftwrappedand gorgeous.co.uk	None	20%	Annual package of £260 and lifetime at £395 which comes with marketing and PR support
Notmassproduced.com	None	20% (starter package), 10% (artisan package)	Starter package is free – allows up to 3 product listings. Artisan package is £55 pa – allows up to 20 product listings.
Bouf.com	None	30% (Free Basic), 20% (Premium).	Premium package is £495/year. With both accounts, also a PayPal fee of 2.5% + 20p per order.

Prices correct at time of publication.

Attract customers to your site through 'search engine optimisation', social tagging and pay-per-click advertising. We look at what these terms mean in the next section and in Week 8 will cover how to market the business in the offline world.

Rise up the search engine ranks

Search Engine Optimisation is commonly referred to as 'SEO' and is the process by which you can improve rankings for your website in the top search engines such as Google, so that your site appears on the first few pages of results rather than page 75!

Google is a search engine that uses software known as 'spiders' to crawl the web on a regular basis and find sites to add to their index. There are steps you can take to make it easier for the spiders to find and add your site.

Start with the homepage

Provide high-quality, text-based content on your pages – especially your homepage. If your homepage has useful information and good quality, relevant text, it's more likely to be picked up by the spiders. Beyond the homepage, write pages that clearly describe your topic/service/product. Think about the words users would type to find your pages, key words, and include them on the site.

Make contributions

Identify influential bloggers and sites in your trade/industry, contact them and offer to write posts. You can also improve your visibility by writing helpful comments in forums and on other people's posts.

Be well connected

Improve the rank of your site by increasing the number of other high-quality sites that link to your pages; these are referred to as 'inbound links'. For example, if you're running a competition, go to sites that promote competitions and add yours.

Register your site with the major search engines.

- Google
  www.google.co.uk/addurl

- Yahoo
  search.yahoo.com/info/submit.html

- Bing
  www.bing.com/webmaster/submitsitepage.aspx

• •

TIP: Search engines love links

Another way to increase your ranking in the search results is to link to other sites and vice versa, but think quality here as opposed to quantity. Sites offering the best 'link juice' are trusted domains, such as news sites, and very popular sites. You could post comments on such sites and blogs and include a link back to your site. Also try these handy hints:

- Approach sites complementary to your own and suggest reciprocal links.

- Ensure that your website link is included in all your social media profiles.

- Register with the major search engines (as explained above).

Add your domain to local search services such as Google Maps, Qype, Yahoo local and BView:

- www.google.co.uk/maps

- www.qype.co.uk

- uk.local.yahoo.com

- www.bview.co.uk

Tagging

A webpage's title, referred to as a 'title tag', is part of the SEO mix and can make a difference to your search rankings. It is also the text that appears in the top of the browser window. Include in your title tag the main key phrase you'd like the search engines to associate with your webpage and keep it to 60–90 characters in length. Duncan Green of Moo Marketing is an SEO expert and explains: "The title tag on the homepage for Moo Marketing reads: 'Moo Marketing – Search Engine Marketing – PPC Management – Search Engine Optimisation'; as you can see, the title element is 85 characters long, contains three key phrases and identifies the subject of the webpage."

Pay-per-click (PPC) advertising

The results from your efforts in SEO will appear on the main engines (Google, Yahoo! and Bing) in the central column of the page as a natural or 'organic' search result. But have you spotted results on the right of the page when searching for items yourself? These are paid-for results and referred to as pay-per-click or PPC advertising. PPC is where you pay to have ads displayed when people type in certain words, in the hope it will attract more visitors to your site.

Google AdWords is such a form of PPC advertising. Think of the key words or phrases you reckon your customers will be searching for and apply them in your Google campaign. Link to your home page or other pages on the site where you're running a promotion and make the most of Geotargeting, which lets you target your ads to specific territories and languages.

You are in full control of the budget and campaign duration.

- adwords.google.co.uk

TIP: Think like a buyer

When thinking of the keywords to use in PPC ad campaigns (and in search engine optimisation) think of the words your buyers will be using when searching for your product or service. Use the Google AdWords Keyword Tool to find out the most popular search terms. Apply these words in the campaign and include them in the text on your site.

CASE STUDY

Name: Alex Hardie

Business: HowDoYouDo Digital Marketing

Started: August 2010

Whilst in employment, Alex Hardie was often asked by small businesses about online marketing techniques. The most popular questions were about social media, email, websites and online PR. Alex realised there was a gap in the knowledge of small business owners around digital marketing tools and techniques. There was also a fear of embracing them.

"HowDoYouDo was born out of my desire to share knowledge of all things online, demystifying them and proving there's nothing to be scared of. It's funny that I've always been looking for ways to make a living from talking to people. And, since we help companies by listening, understanding and having conversations online, I've achieved my first goal."

Alex's first client was his brother, who runs a business handling insurance claims and was in need of a company re-brand and website. Alex comments: "You often rack your brains about how you're going to find new clients, but sometimes forget to look on your own doorstep."

HowDoYouDo now has a roster of clients; Alex is running social media seminars, promoted through Eventbrite, offering companies 'how-to' workshops on social media marketing strategies. He also writes a daily blog, with free marketing hints, tips and tricks, the best of which go out to the company's email database.

"Some people think I'm crazy, giving ideas and knowledge away for free, but actually it drives a massive amount of traffic to my site, which in turn helps it perform better in the search engines. Otherwise I use Facebook, LinkedIn and Twitter to engage with new and existing customers."

Alex's family continue to be involved in the business. He bounces ideas off them, asks for advice in areas he's not so good at (accounting, in Alex's case) and generally they act as a filter for his thoughts.

"Family and friends will always give you an honest answer and that's absolutely invaluable. First and foremost they help keep your feet on the ground."

Alex plans to grow the business over the next 12 months by raising his profile in the area, running more successful events and securing more happy clients. One of the best things of being your own boss, says Alex, is the flexibility to adapt and react to opportunities that were unforeseen – but it's good to start with a plan that guides the direction of the company.

"My advice to anyone considering self-employment is this: know what you do, do it well, believe in it, work at it – you will succeed. So far, it's worked for me!"

- **www.howdoyoudo-marketing.co.uk**
  @hdydmarketing

Spread the word

Make it easy for visitors to spread word of your site through social sharing. Have your site Stumbled, Dugg and Tweeted and make the most of this viral effect. You can add these social book-marking tools by visiting AddThis (www.addthis.com) and choosing the icons you'd like to have displayed on your site.

The most popular are:

- Delicious
  www.delicious.com

- Digg
  www.digg.com

- StumbleUpon
  www.stumbleupon.com

- Twitter
  www.twitter.com

Your website is likely to be the first thing potential customers will see of your business – and they'll make their judgement in seconds! Keep it well polished and visitors will soon become customers.

* *

TIP: A top quality image

Whether you decide to start online with a blog or a full e-commerce site, use high quality royalty-free images on your site and printed materials so that on first click or at first glance, a customer is given a good impression and therefore more likely to buy. Take professional images yourself or consider subscribing to a stock image library such as www.istockphoto.com.

Other image libraries include:

- Image Source
  www.imagesource.com

- Photos.com
  www.photos.com

- Getty Images
  www.gettyimages.com

Search for creative commons licensed images you can use commercially from Flickr at www.compfight.com.

* *

Week 7

Simple sales roadmap and cold-calling made easy

You have your idea. It's supported by research and a plan pointing you in the right direction. You've sorted out all the technology you need to get going. And with the company registered and a good looking online presence, it's time to get into business by making sales and making some noise!

Sell, Sell, Sell!

In this section we'll look at how you achieve a first sale, make a cold call and make money from your website or blog. Follow these five steps to making offline sales.

1. Make a list (check it twice)

Draw on your existing resources, grab your address book and circle the friends, family, colleagues and acquaintances you think might be interested in your product or service. Add to the list with details of local people and businesses, too.

. . . .

TIP: Prospecting for business

To grow your list of sales leads, consider investing in a service such as B2BProspector (www.b2bprospector.co.uk) which offers contact details of potential customers. For example, you might want to contact garden centres in Leicestershire or dentists in Aberdeen – this service will provide you with contact details for your target market.

. . . .

2. Pitch up

Write to the people on your list and announce your new business venture. Consider this an opportunity to make your pitch, but don't be too pushy. And remember to address each recipient personally. No one likes a group email!

3. Follow up

Follow up in a few days time, either with another email or, better still, a phone call. Take some soundings as to the success of your pitch and react accordingly. If the potential customer or client sounds keen, go for it! Arrange to meet him or her to show your product or explain more about your service.

4. Meet up

Arrange a time and place to meet that's convenient for your potential customer or client. Be professional, but also likeable. They're equally important characteristics when making a sale.

If the customer agrees the deal, bring the meeting to a fairly speedy end. Your job is done – for now. It's time to head home and deliver on the promise you made with your first customer.

5. Make some noise

Once you've made your first sale – shout about it! If your new customer or client agrees, include them in a press release or write about them on your website or blog, so other potential customers or clients can see that you're well and truly in business!

TIP: Sales are flying high

Have promotional flyers made to take to events or deliver through doors. Increase chances of turning flyers into firm sales by:

- having a design that is memorable, possibly quirky and, ideally, that your potential customers will want to keep on their desktop/in their purse/atop the kitchen shelf (*see page 137 for advice on having a logo/design that carries across promotion materials*)

- making the offer clear and confirming the benefits of buying

- including a call to action, i.e. a way in which the interested customer can contact you.

Promotional flyers

Getting your message to as many people as possible is key. Flyers are a very cheap and quick way to do this. Staples can print 1,000 A5 flyers in half an hour while you wait – or simply pick them up later to suit you.

Warm up for a cold call

Sales and marketing pro Jackie Wade offers tips on how to make winning calls to customers

Ready: Preparation and focus is key. Avoid time wasting by starting with a clear call list and objectives. Which business or household and who specifically (decision maker)? Are you clear on your message? What benefits do you offer?

Steady: Feel confident, think positive. What's the worst thing that can happen? They may say no... so what! Not everyone out there will want you, but someone will! Tone is as important as words, so feel and sound confident and positive.

Go: Be natural, be you. Have a good opening 'hook' to grab people's attention – something interesting, new or different and make it relevant to the person you're calling. Avoid rambling – focus on a two-way conversation, not a fixed script. Develop a list of open questions which will allow you to engage with the person at the other end of the line, e.g. what do you currently do, how does it work, what might you like to improve? Listen for opportunities. Engage!

Grow: Agree action and follow up promptly or agree a call back, if there's no interest for now. A NO today may be a YES tomorrow; tenacity counts. Things change.

Remember, smile and then dial. Your aim is to spread the word about you and your business.

Jackie Wade is managing director of Winning Sales, www.winningsales.co.uk

. . . .

When making a sales call, do so standing up and smiling. To the person on the other end, you will come across as positive and confident about your product or service.

. . . .

Make sales online

Sales can be made online and off. Attending events and fairs and selling to friends and family is key but you may also want to open your website up to sales. Do so by adding a shopping cart or plugging in an e-commerce tool. Here are some suggestions.

Shopping carts

Add a shopping cart to make life easy for your visitors to click and buy. Check out the shopping cart providers below.

- GroovyCart
  www.groovycart.co.uk

- Zen Cart
  www.zen-cart.com

- RomanCart
  www.romancart.com

- osCommerce
  www.oscommerce.com

- CubeCart
  www.cubecart.com

- Frooition
  www.frooition.com [shopping cart and full website]

Research the product that suits you best, taking into account hosting provision, back-end admin, and built-in search engine optimisation.

E-commerce tools

If you are blogging and want to start selling, consider these plug-in tools that could turn browsers into buyers.

- WordPress e-Commerce shopping cart – "suitable for selling your products, services, and or fees online"
  bit.ly/fEgQHo

- PayPal Shortcodes – insert Paypal buttons in your posts or pages using a shortcode
  bit.ly/eUjhgM

- View a complete list of WordPress e-commerce plugins
  bit.ly/eTEkwZ

Many e-commerce platform sites come with an in-built payment system. Here are the main ones.

PayPal

Regarded as the leading international payment platform, PayPal has more than 84 million active registered accounts and is available in 190 markets, meaning you can successfully trade in all these markets!

For online store owners, PayPal is easy to introduce and offers customers peace of mind that payment will be secure. Indeed, PayPal's Total Payment Volume in 2009 represented nearly 15% of global e-commerce.

The company offers three main products: website payments standard, website payments pro and express checkout. To enable your customers to buy multiple items, use a free PayPal shopping cart. To put the 'Add to Cart' button on your website with HTML code you can simply copy and paste from PayPal to the coding of your own site. Your customers then click the button to make a purchase.

- Add PayPal button
  bit.ly/blxrUn

With PayPal, there are no set-up charges, monthly fees or cancellation charges, and fee levels vary depending on the volume of sales.

- www.paypal.co.uk

Google Checkout

Google Checkout is a global payment system. There are no set-up charges and fees depend on the volume of your sales. With monthly sales of less than $3,000, the fee is currently 2.9% plus $0.30 per transaction. This transaction fee decreases in line with sales volumes increasing.

- checkout.google.com

Sage Pay

Sage Pay is a card payment service that allows you to accept payments by PayPal and major debit and credit cards. It is simple to manage and easy to integrate within your website. The fee is £20 per month for merchants processing up to 1,000 transactions per quarter and 10p per transaction for merchants processing more than 1,000 transactions per quarter, with a minimum charge of £20 per month. There are no set-up fees, no percentage fees and no annual charges.

- www.sagepay.com

TIP: Just-in-time payment

Adding a PayPal payment button to your site will enable you to accept payment from all major credit and debit cards, as well as bank accounts around the world. You can set it up in less than 15 minutes.

For more information on e-commerce, view the video series '10 steps to e-commerce success' produced by Enterprise Nation in association with PayPal: bit.ly/gEdpWO

Distance selling regulations

One thing to bear in mind when selling goods or services to consumers via the internet, mail order or by phone, is compliance with the Consumer Protection (Distance Selling) Regulations 2000. The key features of the regulations are:

- You must offer consumers clear information including details of the goods or services offered, delivery arrangements and payment, the supplier's details and the consumer's cancellation right before they buy (known as prior information). This information should be provided in writing.

- The consumer has a period of seven working days from delivery of the items to cancel their contract with you.

- These regulations only apply when selling to consumers, as opposed to businesses. In the event of a contract being ceased, you have to refund money, including delivery charges, within 30 days of the date of cancellation.

For more guidance, see: bit.ly/aC88pL

On pages 89–90 are five tips to ensure your website is fully and legally compliant.

Keep customers coming back for more with offers and good service, and attract new customers by making some noise! We'll cover these topics in more detail in Weeks 8 and 11.

How to make a profit in a week

A journalist recently called and asked how long it would take a business start-up to turn a profit. "It depends on the business," I replied "but I'd say it's perfectly possible to turn a profit within the week." To try and prove the point I wrote a post about how this could be achieved. Here is that post.

Let's take a business

This feature will not apply to all businesses but let's take the example of someone providing goods and services to consumers (a craft business) and someone offering professional services (a bookkeeper.) This is how they each become profitable by week end.

Example 1: The craft business

Monday
Make item, with cost of raw materials being £5.50.

Photograph item with family camera, ensuring professional/high quality presentation.

Tuesday
Upload profile and photo to three craft sites, which levy a small charge for listing and exercise a sales commission. Sites such as:

Etsy.com – listing fee of 20 cents per item and 3.5% sales commission

MISI.co.uk – listing fee of 20p per item and 3% sales commission

Coriandr.com – listing fee of 20p per item and 2.5% sales commission.

Wednesday
Promote product via Twitter and Facebook. Include a link to the shop so people can click and buy.

Send an email to friends and family (personal, as opposed to group email) to announce the product and, again, link to it in the shop.

Thursday
Upload pictures of your product to Flickr so the large audience there can see it, too.

If you have a webcam, make a short recording of you making products and upload it to YouTube.

Call local stores and boutiques to ask if they would consider selling your stock.

Friday
You've attracted interest and made a sale! Sale price is £25.99.

Cost of making sale	
Raw materials	£5.50
Listing fee	20p
Sales commission:	78p
Marketing and promotion	Your time
Profit for the week	£19.51

Example 2: The bookkeeper

Monday
Start a blog using free blogging platform (e.g. blogger.com or wordpress.com), with helpful posts on bookkeeping technique. This will help you be seen as an expert in your field.

Promote your blog via Twitter, Facebook, etc.

Produce business cards.

Tuesday
Attend a local networking event.

Post on online business forums with helpful bookkeeping advice.

Wednesday
Approach small business sites with an article for them to upload that will interest and assist readers (include a link back to your blog so that people can make contact).

Thursday
Call local accountancy practices to ask if they require outsourced bookkeeping.

Friday

Secure first client! Contract to carry out bookkeeping for local business at rate of £50 per month.

Cost of making sale	
Business cards	£12.99
Promotion and networking	Your time, plus travel costs to events
Profit in first month	£37.01

N.B. This feature is based on user accessing a home/shared/library PC or laptop, so costs of IT equipment are not included.

I was relieved to receive a note three months after this feature was posted from business owner Sharon Bassett, who had taken the advice on board and ... made a profit within the week! Here's how she did it.

Q: Hi Sharon. So, how did you follow the steps in the post?

A: Well, I make a lot of my own soft furnishings, art and accessories at home and your post gave me the idea to use all of the leftover materials on 'mini art' cards and jewellery. So I made some samples and asked for feedback from family and friends and they sold straight away, before I'd even ventured online!

I was inspired by their positive comments and by further orders, so I set up my shop on Coriandr (**www.coriandr.com**), the handmade marketplace you recommended. My shop is called Broderie.

Flickr and Facebook were next. Flickr's brilliant for specialist groups, where your creations can be showcased, but I found that very few of my general networks were tapping into this. The gap was easily filled by setting up a free Facebook Page. Actually, a good tip is to establish a 'vanity URL' for your Facebook. It's easier to communicate than a long URL. Just go to **www.facebook.com/username** and follow the instructions.

In terms of local boutiques, some of my products are currently being considered on a sale or return basis. One boutique that stocks some basic items I need for my jewellery products has offered to purchase them for me at a price cheaper than I have found anywhere else.

Q: If you don't mind us asking, how much profit did you make in the first week?

A: I made £23.50 after purchasing card blanks at £3.49. I was delighted!

Q: Are you going to carry on making and selling your 'mini art'?

A: Absolutely! I've made my own business cards, and I'm full of ideas for new designs. I've found a few local networking events and craft fairs to go to. And a local business is featuring Broderie in its newsletter next month. I've still got Twitter and YouTube to master! But I'm getting there...

- **www.coriandr.com/shop/broderie**

Read pages 149–153 for guidance on how you can get up and running using tools such as Twitter, Facebook and Flickr.

Make money from your website/blog

If your product is your website or blog, sell its content and/or parts of your online space. As traffic to your online home increases, so also do your chances of generating income. Make a profit from your posts with this top-ten list of options.

1. Display advertising

Offer advertising on your site. The more niche your audience, the more likely you are to attract advertisers.

The information you'll need to provide includes:

- number of unique visitors
- number of impressions
- average duration of visit
- visitor demographics.

Write a basic rate card, add it to your site and send it to corporate marketing departments and media-buying agencies.

TIP: Show me your rates!

The purpose of a media rate card is to show potential advertisers what your site can deliver to them in terms of traffic and possible sales. To do this, include some key points:

A brief description of the site: What it does and for whom.

Visitor demographics: Do you have data on the age of your site visitors, their home region, gender, etc? If so, include it, as it helps build a picture of your audience.

Site traffic: What are your unique visitor numbers and length of time spent on the site? Include a note or graph if the figures are increasing.

Costings: Do you have a cost-per-click (CPC) or cost-per-impression (CPM) rate? If so, include it here, along with the price of other sponsorship options. Offer a menu but leave some flexibility, with 'costed on a project basis' for sponsor features that would benefit from a more tailored proposal.

Screen shots: Showing how and where adverts or sponsored features appear on the site.

Media activity: Note where you've recently been covered in the media, online and off, so that potential sponsors can see how and where you're promoting the site.

Testimonials: Positive comments from existing sponsors give credibility to you and confidence to the next potential sponsor.

Team details: Who are the faces behind the site and what are their credentials? In other words, your background career and activities, etc.

Round this off with your contact details so that anyone interested can get in touch and place an order!

2. Google AdSense

This tool from Google does the work for you in that it places relevant ads on your site and earns you money when people click on them. You can customise the appearance of the ads so they sit well with the style of your site.

- www.google.co.uk/adsense

3. TextLinkAds

These ads offer direct click-throughs from text on your site. You submit your site to TextLinkAds and then upload the ad code provided. It's your choice whether you approve or deny the supplied ads. Once that's done, you start making money as visitors click on the ads. Try this and Skimlinks, which converts words on your site to affiliate links so that you earn from those, too.

- www.text-link-ads.com

- www.skimlinks.com

4. Sponsored conversations

Get paid for posts (and now tweets) with services like izea.com that match bloggers with advertisers. Some doubt the ethical stance of paying a blogger to write something about a product but there's no doubt that it's a money maker.

- www.izea.com

5. Affiliate schemes

Sign up to affiliate schemes like the Amazon Associates programme, where you can earn up to 10% in referrals by advertising Amazon products. The programme works by driving traffic to Amazon.co.uk through specially formatted links. You earn referral fees on sales generated through those links. Monthly cheques are sent to you from Amazon and it's easy and free to join.

- affiliate-program.amazon.co.uk

6. Sponsored features

This could include a host of options. Approach advertisers with suggestions of a sponsored eBook, e-news, podcast, webchat, poll or survey. These applications can be added to your site at a low cost yet generate good revenue. See pages 132–6 for details on how these features can help you become an expert in your field. For:

- eBook creation, try www.blurb.com

- a survey or poll feature, try www.surveymonkey.com

- email marketing, try www.mailchimp.com.

7. Expert help

Offer your expertise and charge people to log on and watch or listen. This could be made available through:

Teleclasses
Invite customers and contacts on to a call where you offer your expertise on a one-to-many basis. Check out Karen Skidmore's 'How to get started with Teleclasses' at bit.ly/hg4fea.

GoToWebinar
Deliver a presentation to potentially thousands of paying customers via www.gotowebinar.co.uk.

8. Deals with suppliers

Do deals with suppliers. Hosting a travel blog? Agree a percentage each time a booking is made via your site. Hosting a shedworking blog? Create a directory that includes all garden office suppliers but with an enhanced listing for those who pay.

9. Turn a blog into a book

Follow the lead of Sue Hedges and Angela Savchenko who had their blog Moan About Men (www.moanaboutmen.com) turned into a book, which is now selling across the UK and acting as an effective marketing tool for the site!

10. Please donate

If you'd rather just ask for a small donation from your visitors, this is possible too via a donate feature from PayPal. Add a PayPal donate button to your site: bit.ly/ikf832

Week 8

Make some noise!

Sales are coming in and you want to tell the world about you and your new business. Profile brings new customers, new sales and headlines!

Getting Known

Become known in the press and online by making friends with the media, hosting events, entering awards and becoming an expert in your field. Create the right first impression, whether a customer meets you at an event or visits you online. Here's guidance on how to achieve it all. First step: getting known.

Plot the script

Imagine yourself as the star of your own Hollywood movie. Are you an action hero, battling against the odds (think James Dyson) or a brand-leading lady (think Nigella Lawson)? Plot the action and write the script. It will help you define your message to the media.

Find the right contacts

Research the journalists you think are interested in your field. Note their email addresses from the bottom of their articles, follow them on Twitter, get to know them and send them exclusive stories about you and your business.

● ●

TIP: Following the media

Follow media contacts and channels on Twitter to pick up on profile opportunities. Here are a few from radio/TV/magazines:

- @BBCBreakfast
- @BBCOnTheMoney
- @talktothepress
- @findaTVexpert
- @TheTimesLive
- @guardian

● ●

Please contact Enterprise Nation with your story as we are always profiling start-ups and small businesses on our website, in books (like this one!), in kits, in videos and as part of the national StartUp Britain campaign.

Submit your story at www.enterprisenation.com.

Write a release

Writing a press release costs nothing but your time, yet it can generate thousands of pounds worth of publicity. If you're emailing a press release to journalists, write the text in the body of the email and include it in an attachment, too.

Your press release should have an attention-grabbing headline, the main facts in the first sentence and evidence and quotes from as high-profile people and companies as possible in the main body of the text. Include great quality images wherever you can to lift the piece and put a face to the brand (but don't make the email file size huge!). You could also use a press-release distribution service to secure wider exposure. My personal favourite is Response Source (www.responsesource.com) but there's also PR Newswire (www.prnewswire.co.uk) and PRWeb (www.prweb.com).

If you don't get a response, follow up!

● ●

TIP: Link request

If you're being featured online ask the journalist if they can include a live link to your site. That way, readers can be on your site within a click.

● ●

PR is the perfect kick start!

Equipped with some simple PR know-how, you can really put yourself on the map. Louise Findlay-Wilson, creator of PrPro, offers some quick techniques

Be familiar – get to know the media that matters: the media your customers and prospects read, listen to or look at online.

Back to basics – aim to put out 12 news stories a year. Prepare your basic stories (launch of a new product / award win / company development / interesting case study etc.) in the form of a punchy news release – 300 words max. Always apply the 'so what' rule when writing. If the audience isn't likely to care about your story then don't waste time writing it!

Be opinionated – don't just rely on news. What's topical; what's challenging your customers that you can legitimately have an opinion on? Your big competitors will be bland bland bland! Have personality.

Create news – short of news? Create it. Host an event, run a poll or a competition. Or maybe deliver a seminar or write an expert guide.

My way – tell your story: the media may like to tell it too.

Join the dots – if you get online exposure, tweet about it, link to it, use it in your social media activity.

Persist – don't give up!

Louise Findlay-Wilson is a PR pro and creator of PrPro, www.prpro.co.uk

TIP: An image speaks louder than words

When a picture speaks a thousand words you can afford to talk less! Consider hiring a professional photographer to take pictures of you and your work. Maybe you can do this as a barter deal? Pick up your own digital camera and do it yourself or contact your local college and ask if any photography students would like to offer their time so you receive a free image and the student has material for their portfolio. A journalist is much more likely to cover your story if you have great imagery to go with it. Use the images on your website and in promotion materials and let your business speak for itself.

Example press release

1. Attention-grabbing headline.

2. The first line is punchy and explains the what, who, why and where of the headline.

3. Back up the headline and first sentence with facts and figures, or other greater detail.

4. Include a quote from you (or a key figure involved in the business).

5. Include the vital information about where can people go to find out more/how to download the report/which site to visit to claim a free gift, etc.

6. Can you include a quote from someone else? A happy customer, industry expert or celebrity? (Or yourself, if you were not quoted earlier.)

7. Include 'Media notes', with brief details on you and your company.

8. Remember to include contact details – your email address and telephone number.

9. Attach a relevant and interesting image.

1.

2.

3.

4.

5.

6.

7.

8.

SATURDAY CLUB LAUNCHED TO HELP PEOPLE BECOME THEIR OWN BOSS

A UK retailer is putting its full weight behind the StartUp Britain campaign in an effort to create a 500,000-strong army of entrepreneurs to help get the economy moving.

Staples will host weekly classes in its 138 stores for those who want to become their own boss – giving over prime retail space on a Saturday morning.

Start Up Saturday will run for 12 weeks, covering everything from discovering your big idea right through to finance and marketing on a shoestring.

Staples Managing Director Andrew Gabriel said: "The StartUp Britain Campaign has gathered momentum and really inspired people to think about launching their own venture. But we want to help them do more than think about it and believe StartUp Saturday can play a key role in turning great ideas into real businesses.

"Hopefully by holding the sessions in our stores we will break down the barriers to classroom learning and people of all ages will feel comfortable in signing up."

StartUp Saturday, which is being run by the small business advice company Enterprise Nation and training providers CragRats, will be launched in six stores on May 21, before being rolled out across the country from June.

Each session will be from 9.30am to 10.30am and students will be given a comprehensive workbook, which will include advice, case studies, useful links and tips. Individual classes cost just £10 and the full 12-week course is £100. Book courses online at www.startupsaturday.com.

Emma Jones, of Enterprise Nation and one of the founders of StartUp Britain, said: "There's no time like the present to start a business. We know there's a wealth of talent out there and that all people need is a kick start, which is what this initiative is all about. The course will be fun and hopefully lead to financial reward and a flexible working life."

Media notes

9.

StartUp Saturday is a weekly class held in Staples stores from 9.30 to 10.30am. Classes are delivered by small business support company, Enterprise Nation, and training provider, CragRats.

StartUp Britain is a national campaign to encourage more people to start a business and support existing businesses to grow.

For media enquiries, please contact Emma Jones at emma@enterprisenation.com or call (01234) 567 8910.

TIP: Monkeying around

Run a poll with, for example, Wufoo or Survey Monkey, which is free to use, and publish the results via a press release and online. The media loves good polls!

- www.surveymonkey.com
- www.wufoo.com

CASE STUDY

Name: Ella Gascoigne
Business: Startup PR
Started: July 2009

Ella Gascoigne spent three years heading up PR for a publishing company in London and in that role worked with many entrepreneurs, promoting business books and publications.

"I was immersed in the start-up world and I loved it!"

In 2008 Ella was made redundant and her world changed. After covering maternity leave for the PR manager at Friends Reunited, Ella decided she was fed up of working long hours in London. She moved to Yorkshire, to return to her family and in search of a better life.

"Being made redundant made me realise that as long as I worked for other people, I would not be in control of my own life and career – I would never really be free to succeed (or fail). I wanted work freedom and realised the only way to achieve this would be to set up my own business. I had met many entrepreneurs, authors and small business owners and I loved the start-up space. So I considered what I could offer to this community."

Ella contacted all the small business owners she knew and asked if they used a PR service – and if not, why not? Many start-ups said they didn't use a PR agent because they didn't feel it would be a good return on their investment. Many businesses didn't have the budget for an in-house PR team and they didn't want the commitment of a retainer fee and the high costs often charged by an agency.

"What I did see was that these new businesses nevertheless needed to get publicity to launch and grow their business. I spotted a gap in the market and launched Startup PR – publicity to grow your business, offering affordable, flexible PR for small businesses."

Without a budget of her own to start with, Ella borrowed a laptop until she could save enough money to buy one. She negotiated a free website and business cards with a designer in return for giving them some free PR! And she worked from home – decorating the attic room to have a separate space – to cut out the overheads of an office.

"I have Roland the cat and Tokolosh the dog for colleagues (although their tea-making skills are not quite up to scratch)."

Ella's marketing was based on word of mouth and social media. She emailed all her contacts to tell them she had set up in business. She set up Twitter, Facebook and LinkedIn accounts and started engaging with small businesses, offering free 'advice' as well as a 20-minute free PR clinic.

"This all paid off. And, with recommendations, by October 2009 I was working to full capacity, getting results and having to turn down work!"

Ella soon needed help as she had so much work. She employed other freelance PRs who also worked from home, and so avoided the costs that come with employing staff. To meet people (not just for work but also to get out of the house and settle in her new community) Ella volunteered to help with a local festival; she's now been on the organising committee for the past two years. It was through volunteering that she met another businesswoman and together they have started a support network for women in and around Harrogate.

"Starting the network was never about making money or growing my business but it has been hugely beneficial to Startup PR. It was a great way for me to build my own profile and promote my business within the area – the media coverage it gained was excellent and it also provided a support network to help all of the members."

In just under a year Ella's business has grown from an idea to serving 12 regular clients. Ella has promoted a range of high-profile books and her clients have been on TV shows, radio programmes, in magazines and on popular blogs.

"Above all, I am most proud of what my clients say about me."

And this is not a bad testimonial to have: "Ella is smart, reliable and a pleasure to work with; she understands the subtleties you need working in PR," says Dave Stewart (entrepreneur and Eurythmics musician).

- **www.startuppr.co.uk**
  @startupprella

Enter awards

Enter awards and competitions and enjoy the press coverage that goes with it. Many award schemes are free to enter and are targeted at young start-up businesses. Writing the entry will help to clarify your goals and vision, and winning will bring profile and prizes.

To find out about upcoming awards, visit www.awardsintelligence.co.uk or check out the following:

- Shell LiveWIRE Grand Ideas Awards – up to six awards per month of £1,000 for anyone aged 16 to 30 looking to get an idea off the ground.
  www.shell-livewire.org/awards

- Ambition AXA Awards – a prize of £40,000 for someone between the age of 11 and 18 who wants to launch a business. That's quite a start-up sum!
  www.ambitionaxaawards.com

- The Pitch 2011 – enter regional heats and pitch to experienced judges for a place in the national finals. Takes place across the UK.
  www.thepitch2011.com

- *Country Living* Magazine Kitchen Table Talent Awards – if you're working on a talent or skill from the kitchen table and know it can be turned into a business, this competition is for you. Prizes include office equipment, profile in the magazine and a year's mentoring from the author of this very workbook!
  bit.ly/i458Vj

- Social Enterprise Awards – celebrates social enterprises of all ages.
  www.socialenterprise.org.uk/pages/social-enterprise-awards.html

- Nectar Small Business Awards – offers cash prizes and plenty of Nectar points!
  bit.ly/goTAti

- Startups Awards – celebrating small businesses of all shapes and sizes.
  www.startupsawards.co.uk

Read in the next case study how Nick Proctor benefited from having his business profiled as part of the Shell LiveWIRE Young Entrepreneur of the Year Awards.

CASE STUDY

Name: Nick Proctor

Business: Amber Energy Consultants

Started: August 2009

After leaving university, Nick Proctor started working for a large high street bank. When the recession hit and the bank was viewed in a new light, Nick reconsidered his comfy sales job, gave up his salary and company car, and started his own business. He's now boss of Amber Energy Consultants and relishing each day and opportunity.

"We provide a service to businesses looking to lower their energy costs. We do this in two ways; achieving a more competitive rate on their current level of energy usage and working with the business to lower their usage. We also focus on various accreditations that businesses can work towards, such as Carbon Neutral company status, and/or Planet Positive accredited."

Nick came up with the idea for the company after researching the market for energy advice and deeming it to be 'overwhelming' – with a large number of different companies offering seemingly different products, advice, and information.

"Our customers know where to turn and what steps they should be taking to lower their energy costs and/or carbon footprint. We make this information readily available to clients and have just launched monthly podcasts which will later form a full guide to energy management."

In starting the business, Nick has done everything himself; from developing and building a website using online guides, to working on a strategy to develop his services and access bigger businesses. With a vision to become the trusted business partner for all things energy related, he wants to grow the business by providing an unbeatable service without compromising on core principles.

"We value all our clients and it's essential to our business success that clients use us again (and hopefully again!)."

The company is being promoted via various channels: direct mailshots, email, telephone calls, web promotions, Google AdWords, referrals from existing customers, and incentivised referrals from third parties. They have a LinkedIn presence, with Facebook and Twitter developments underway!

Promotion activity focuses on offering a compelling reason for customers to 'trial' Amber Energy Consultants, with a free or complementary offer. Amber will provide a guide, assessment or review and from there on Nick has to deliver beyond expectations so the relationship can be nurtured into a fee-paying client.

"I am loving the challenge and get great satisfaction from a hard days work. Being my own boss has taught me to separate being a director of a company and an employee."

And the one thing Nick most enjoys? "Working from home and having the shortest ever walk to work!"

- **www.amberenergy.net**

Host an event

Invite the press to come and meet you. This doesn't have to be an expensive affair; the secret is partnering with others who would benefit from being in front of your audience. Approach a venue and ask if they would host at no cost, in exchange for the venue receiving profile. Do the same with caterers. Then give invited guests a reason to attend – have a theme, an interesting speaker, a launch announcement, something that will grab their attention and encourage them to attend.

Make use of free online services such as Eventbrite (www.eventbrite.com) or MeetUp (www.meetup.com) to send out invites and receive rsvps.

TIP: I'm a celebrity. Get me on your product!

One way to attract profile and attention is to have a celebrity endorse your product or service. Lyndsey Young has seen the benefit of this. She is the inventor of Count On It food freshness labels and she secured an endorsement from celebrity mum and actress Amanda Holden, who has used the labels when preparing meals for her daughter. This support has been beneficial in leading to other marketing successes, including features in BBC *Easy Cook*, *Your Homes*, *That's Life*, *Cook Vegetarian* and *Healthy* magazine.

Join a group or club

Signing up to a local business club or network is good for business and your social life. You get together to do deals but also end up making friends. Check out these national business networks to find your natural fit.

- 1230 TWC – events for women in business.
  www.1230.co.uk

- 4Networking – national network of business breakfast groups.
  www.4networking.biz

- The Athena Network – networking organisation for women in business.
  www.theathenanetwork.com

- Business Scene – hosts regional and national networking events as well as hosting an online directory of over 10,000 events across the UK.
  www.business-scene.com

- Ecademy – national site with local and regional meet-ups.
  www.ecademy.com

- Jelly – an American import which encourages casual gatherings of co-workers, with events held in people's homes, the local coffee shop or workspaces. The idea is that you meet in relaxed surroundings and creative ideas are stimulated by the experience. There are now Jelly events taking place in all corners of the UK. In March 2011 The Big Jelly was the first ever gathering of Jelly organisers. Visit www.uk-jelly.org.uk/uk-big-jelly to find out about the organisers and event plans for next year!
  www.uk-jelly.org.uk

- School for Startups – headed by serial entrepreneur Doug Richard, School for Startups travels the UK hosting events for anyone considering starting a business. Gems from Doug's presentations are broadcast via S4STV.
  www.schoolforstartups.co.uk

- Women in Rural Enterprise (WiRE) – networking and business club for rural women in business.
  www.wireuk.org

- First Friday – a free business networking event held monthly; an informal gathering in a welcoming environment.
  www.firstfriday-network.co.uk

There are also chambers, associations, trade groups and enterprise agencies who host regular events:

- British Chambers of Commerce
  www.britishchambers.org.uk

- Federation of Small Businesses (FSB)
  www.fsb.org.uk

- Forum of Private Business
  www.fpb.org

- NFEA, the national enterprise network
  www.nfea.com

- Professional Contractors Group (PCG)
  www.pcg.org.uk

National bodies that hold events and offer support at certain stages in your entrepreneurial career include:

- National Council for Graduate Entrepreneurship – a body responsible for encouraging new start-ups and an entrepreneurial mindset amongst students and graduates up to five years out of education.
  www.ncge.com

- National Enterprise Academy – started by *Dragons' Den* entrepreneur Peter Jones, the academy offers a full-time educational course and qualification in enterprise and entrepreneurship for 16-19 year olds.
  www.thenea.org

- PRIME (The Prince's Initiative for Mature Enterprise) – a network for the over 50s that provides free information, events and training. PRIME also offers loans through an innovative scheme with online lender Zopa and the charitable arm of Bank of America.
  www.prime.org.uk
  www.primebusinessclub.co.uk

From attending events you may meet businesses with whom there is a shared opportunity. See pages 164–5 for details on how to draw up a basic partnership agreement.

Attend trade shows

Promote your brand by attending the shows your customers attend. Research the best shows by reading industry magazines and visiting online forums where people in your sector are talking.

Tradeshow tactics

Before the event
Negotiate a good deal – if you're prepared to wait it out, the best deals on stands can be had days before the event is starting. The closer the date, the better the price you'll negotiate as the sales team hurry to get a full house.

Tell people you're going – circulate news that you'll be at the event through online networks (giving your location or stand number) and issue a press release if you're doing something newsworthy at the event, maybe launching a new product, having a guest appearance, running a competition, etc.

At the event
Be clear on the offer – determine what you are selling at the show and let this be consistent across show materials; from pop-up stands to flyers. Be creative with the stand to keep costs low. Consider offering a supply of mouth-watering refreshments!

Pop-ups

Pop-ups get your business noticed, especially if you're hoping to stand out at an exhibition or a trade show. Staples' Copy & Print Centres can take your design and turn it into a versatile, portable sign in less than an hour.

Collect data – find ways to collect attendees' names and details. Offer a prize in exchange for business cards or take details in exchange for a follow-up information pack or offer. Some events also offer the facility to scan the details from the delegates' badges (for a fee).

Take friends/family – invite a supportive team. If you're busy talking to a potential customer, you'll want others on the stand who can be doing the same. If there's time, get to know the exhibitors around you.

Be prepared – wear comfortable shoes, bring some spare clothes and pack your lunch; if you're busy there may not be time to spend buying food and drink!

After the event

Follow-up – within a couple of days of returning from the show, contact the people who expressed interest so that interest can be turned into sales.

Plan ahead – if the show delivered a good return, contact the organisers and ask to be considered for a speaking slot or higher profile at the next event, and confirm your willingness to be a case study testimonial story in any post-show promotion.

Become an expert

Set yourself up as an expert in your field and the media will come knocking on your door. Do this by writing a book, offering training or developing your own app! Here are eight ways in which you can promote your expertise.

1. Publish a book

Become a published author on the topic of your choice by self-publishing via sites such as Lulu, Blurb and Ubyu. Utilise the book as a business development tool, printing on demand to take copies to events, and offering free and downloadable versions to potential customers. Being an author gives you credibility and gives customers information and insight.

- Blurb
  www.blurb.com

- Lulu
  www.lulu.com

- Ubyu
  www.ubyubooks.com

2. Present yourself

Put yourself forward to speak at events (consider asking for a fee and/or costs to be covered) or suggest being a satellite speaker, where you are beamed into the conference hall via video link-up, so saving the effort and expense of travel. Invite customers and prospects and make the presentation openly available via Slideshare.

- Slideshare.com
  www.slideshare.com

3. Host a webinar

Share your expertise or demonstrate a process by hosting a webinar or visual presentation where a 'live' audience can see you and interact. Achieve this via platforms such as GoToMeeting, GoToWebinar, Webex and Salesforce, and remember to host it at a time that suits your target audience.

- GoToMeeting
  www.gotomeeeting.com

- GoToWebinar
  www.gotomeeting.com/fec/webinar

- Webex
  www.webex.co.uk

- Salesforce
  www.salesforce.com

4. Produce a film

Maybe the word 'film' is a little ambitious but you can create your own video content with an affordable camcorder or smart phone, or by hiring in a cameraman and having a sponsored series of guides that can be uploaded to video sharing sites such as YouTube, Vimeo and eHow, and easily embedded into your site.

- YouTube
  www.youtube.com

- Vimeo
  www.vimeo.com

- eHow
  www.ehow.co.uk

5. Broadcast a podcast

For customers who like to listen to what you have to say at a time that suits them, upload a podcast with top tips, interviews and your thoughts of the day. Make it available on your site, iTunes and Podcast Alley to be sure of a wide audience. Follow advice from podcast producer San Sharma on how to record a podcast on a Skype call.

- Submit a podcast to the iTunes store
  www.apple.com/itunes/podcasts/specs.html

- Podcast Alley
  www.podcastalley.com

• •

TIP: How to record a podcast on a Skype call

You can produce a podcast interview using Skype, Pamela Call Recorder, and a little editing know-how. San Sharma shows how it's done, in five simple steps...

1. Sign up for a free Skype account (www.skype.com) and download the Skype software.

2. If you're using a Windows machine, download Pamela Call Recorder (www.pamela.biz), which lets you record your Skype calls. If you're on a Mac, you can download Call Recorder for Skype (www.ecamm.com). Both have free trial versions, but only cost around £13 when that's expired.

3. Call up your interviewee using Skype. If they're a Skype user, too, that will be a free call but if they're on a fixed or mobile line, you'll need to get some Skype Credit (bit.ly/epymNm).

4. Once you've made a connection and agreed with the interviewee the format of the conversation, hit the record button on your call recorder software and you're off!

5. Edit using Audacity (audacity.sourceforge.net), which is free for Windows and Macs, or with GarageBand (www.apple.com/ilife/garageband), which comes with most Macs (you can also buy it as part of the iLife package).

And the easiest way to share your recording is by uploading it to AudioBoo (www.audioboo.com), which lets people listen to it on the web, embedded on your website or via iTunes or a mobile phone.

San Sharma is online community manager at Enterprise Nation
(www.enterprisenation.com)

6. Deliver training

Whether your skill is in embroidering handmade shoes or developing stylish websites, your knowledge could be shared with others. Rather than seeing this as surrendering intelligence to potential competitors, offer instruction you're comfortable with that will create fans and followers who will learn from you, buy from you and, critically, encourage others to do the same. Check out platforms GoToTraining and Webtraining, encourage contacts to sign up and then after the demonstration you have a chance to follow up with a group of new contacts.

- GoToTraining
  www.gotomeeting.com/fec/training/online_training

- WebEx Webtraining
  www.webex.co.uk/product-overview/training-center.html

7. Develop an app

Take your content and make an iPhone app with browser-based platform Appmakr. It's free to use and you can either set a list price to make sales via the App Store or make it available free of charge.

- Appmakr
  www.appmakr.com

8. Form groups

Encourage others to discuss, debate and contribute to your content by forming groups utilising social media platforms such as Facebook, LinkedIn and Ning. Bonding interested people to each other will bond them ever closer to you, the content creator and group host.

- Facebook
  www.facebook.com

- LinkedIn
  www.linkedin.com

- Ning
  www.ning.com

TIP: Be everywhere

Keep in touch with existing customers via a newsletter and reach out to the new by making regular appearances at events, on other people's websites and blogs, in newspapers and magazines, and on radio and TV. Write to the magazines and radio stations that ask people to send in their story. It's a free way to get coverage. The more you're covered, the more you'll be invited to speak and comment, and before you know it, you'll be everywhere!

Price point

These publishing options will raise your profile but you can also generate revenue from them. Your options are:

- make your content and knowledge available at no charge to customers, to build your reputation as the go-to person and place for a particular product or service

- charge for access/downloads/viewing and turn your micropublishing activity into a revenue stream in its own right.

Individual judgement will be needed in this and it's something you can assess over time. Start with a mix of charged-for and free content, ensure you are providing good value and incentives for your community to remain engaged, and the options to introduce charged-for content will increase.

First Impressions Count

Your marketing activity is going to plan and the business is attracting interest and enquiries from potential customers. Greet them in a professional way and make that first impression count.

Look at my logo!

Customers will get an immediate sense of your style from your logo and company branding. Impress with a nice-looking company design that's repeated across promotion materials, from business cards to brochures.

Think about what you'd like as your company font, colours and layout. Have a go at designing this yourself or hire the services of a designer/neighbour/friend. Good presentation can make a world of difference. And it may just be the difference you need to clinch a contract.

Find a professional to design your logo via these sites:

- Crowdspring
  www.crowdspring.com

- 99 designs
  www.99designs.com

- Bitsy
  www.bitsythis.com

- Concept Cupboard
  www.conceptcupboard.com

Office address

If you are running your business from home there are a couple of reasons why you might not want to put the address on your business card: it might sound too domestic, and you might not want people turning up on your doorstep!

You can solve this with a P.O. Box number, which starts at £60 per year and is easily set up with Royal Mail (www.royalmail.com). Alternatively, you could invest in a virtual office, which gives you a more tailored and personal service than a P.O. Box – plus you get a nice-sounding address and a place to meet other home business owners and clients. Having a virtual office enables you to choose the address that suits you best, have post delivered to that location, and then forwarded on to you. Companies providing this service include:

- Regus
  www.regus.com

- Mail Boxes Etc.
  www.mbe.co.uk

- eOffice
  www.eoffice.net

When holding meetings, consider hiring professional meeting space. Many offer serviced addresses and secretarial services too, so there could be great continuity for your clients if they only have to remember one location.

• •

Make the most of the email marketing opportunity every time you click 'send'. Include a professional email signature or sign-off that has your basic contact details (name, company, postal address, telephone, etc.) and also maybe mention any seasonal or product offers. Indeed, you are required by law, following the introduction of the Companies Act 2006, to display the company's registered office address on your website and any electronic communications.

• •

On the phone

When running a business from home, consider who will be picking up the phone! It's cheap and sometimes free to get an 0845 local rate number or an 0870 national rate number for your business. This will hide where you're based and divert your calls to wherever you specify. But beware: sometimes having such a number – especially with national rates – might put customers off ringing you.

If you use a landline number it's best to have a separate line for your home and your business. It will stop your business calls from being answered by the kids and also give you a chance to escape work calls when you want to. And these days you don't need to invest in an actual second line. I use a VoIP (voice over internet protocol) phone, which uses my broadband internet connection to make and receive calls, something we looked at earlier (page 73).

- Skype
  www.skype.com

Another idea is to get some help from a call-handling service. They will answer your calls with your company name, text urgent messages to you and email the others, giving you a big business feel for about £50 per month. I use a service called Moneypenny, but there are other providers too, including Regus and Answer.

- Moneypenny
  www.moneypenny.biz

- Regus
  www.regus.co.uk

- Answer
  www.answer.co.uk

You might consider a 'follow-me number' to ensure you're available when you need to be and able to deliver the right impression to clients. A follow-me number involves choosing a number and directing calls from it to your landline or mobile. The beauty of choosing a number is that you have the option to select either a freephone or a geographical number so, say you'd like to have a Manchester area code, simply buy a number starting with 0161. The same goes for hundreds of other locations.

Route calls to your mobile and choose a local number in any of 21 countries to have a virtual local presence with Skype (www.skype.com). Offer virtual phone numbers where the caller pays a local rate, regardless of where you are, through Vonage (www.vonage.co.uk) or direct calls to you from a chosen number using internet technology and a virtual receptionist at eReceptionist (www.ereceptionist.co.uk).

In print

Print is far from dead, so get yourself some business cards, postcards and promotion flyers to hand out at business events, social occasions, and to just about anyone you meet! Have fun with designing your materials and including images relating to your trade. Sell vintage fashion? Include pictures of your products. Offer web design services? Have a portfolio of sites you've designed nicely displayed.

Business cards

It used to be a bit of a palaver to get business cards printed, as well as expensive. First there was a designer to brief, you had to order a thousand at a time and they often took weeks to arrive. These days you can pop into Staples' Copy & Print Centre, tell them what you want and they can print a set in minutes, while you wait – or you can come back later to collect.

●●●

TIP: A memorable exchange

Richard Moross, founder of MOO.com, says:

"The point of having a business card is to: make a connection, create a relationship and leave something with the recipient that reminds them of you.

"Have cards that tell a story. Use that card as a sales tool, for sure, but also show appreciation by having cards relating to your customer."

Richard Moross achieves this by having images on his cards showing places he's visited and meals he's eaten. With 70% of MOO.com's business being outside the UK, Richard travels a lot and the cards act as the ice breaker in meetings as he tells the story behind the pictures.

●●●

In person

You are about to attend your first networking event or trade show and want to create a good first impression. With an attractive business card in hand, directing prospective customers to a good-looking online presence, all you have to do is follow the rules of effective networking!

The art of networking

- Wear your name tag (if you have one) on your right side. It's easy to catch sight of when you are shaking hands.

- Deliver a nice firm handshake and make eye contact.

- Say your name clearly and, in under ten seconds, tell the other person who you are and what you do.

- Listen carefully. Ask the other person plenty of questions about their line of business, their family, their hobbies, without being too intrusive or personal.

- Be positive and energetic.

- Swap business cards.

- Send a 'thank you' email after the event, confirming any actions you and they have promised.

- Keep in regular, and meaningful, contact.

See pages 129–130 for details of networking groups to join, pages 128–9 for information on how to host your own event, and page 131 for how to attend a trade show to promote the business.

Template 7: Marketing and Promotion Checklist

Media

Press

National press	*Insert your list of target titles here*
Regional and local press	*Insert your list of target titles here*
Trade press	*Insert your list of target titles here*

Radio

Insert programmes on which you'd like to appear

Television

Insert programmes on which you'd like to appear

Magazines

Insert your list of target titles here

Online

Websites	*Insert list of sites for reciprocal links*
Blogs	*Insert list of blogs on which you'll comment*

Press releases

Press hook stories	*Insert list of press stories for the year*
Images to attach	*Insert list of images you have, or need to get, for each release*

Other

Events

Insert list of events to attend; networking and trade. Aim for speaking opportunities. What about hosting your own event, too?

Awards

Insert list of awards relevant to your business and their dates of entry

Week 9

5 essential social media tools and how to make the most of them

There have never been so many tools at our disposal that we can use to promote our business free of charge, and without a significant outlay of time. I'm talking about social media. It's time to embrace it.

Embrace Social Media

According to research company Nielsen, the world now spends over 110 billion minutes on social networks and blogs per month. This equates to 22% of all time online, or one in every four and half minutes.

Embrace this and your business will become known. Here are the five key tools to use and, crucially, how best to use them.

Twitter

Visit www.twitter.com, create an account, start to follow friends and contacts (and their followers) and get tweeting. Follow Mark Shaw's steps for Twitter success.

- Cost: free

● ●

TIP: How to be a success on Twitter

Twitter expert Mark Shaw shares his four top tips that will have you tweeting like a pro.

1. Be committed
Add a good photo, perhaps a bespoke background, your website URL and an interesting bio. Try and differentiate yourself and make sure the bio contains keywords so that others can find you.

2. Be consistent
Show up each day, and tweet, even if time is short. It's more important to do a small amount each day than lots one day and then nothing for a week or so.

3. Be interesting
Try and tweet three types of messages: social chit-chat; the sharing of resources, links, tools, info, ideas and opinions; and tweets that answer questions which demonstrate your knowledge. Aim for a good balance.

4. Be interested

Engage with others by answering questions and joining in. Find conversations to enter into via search.twitter.com and retweet (RT) other people's messages if they are of interest to you and your followers. It's not about selling things but it is all about building your brand and credibility.

Mark Shaw
@markshaw
www.markshaw.biz

● ●

Facebook

Facebook is the most popular social networking site in the world. The site has over 500 million users worldwide, so if you need to be where your customers are, there's a good chance some of them will be there!

You can list on Facebook for free and/or advertise on the site and select an audience based on location, age and interest. As an advertiser, you control how much you want to spend and set a daily budget. The minimum budget is US $1.00 (63p) a day. After designing your ad(s), decide for how long you want the campaign to run and whether you want to be charged for the number of clicks you receive (CPC – charge per click) or the number of times your ad is displayed. Visit www.facebook.com, create an account, invite friends and contacts to join your group and get promoting.

● Listing cost: free

LinkedIn

Referring to itself as "the world's largest professional network", LinkedIn has 75 million members in over 200 countries. Visit www.linkedin.com, create an account and start connecting with contacts and finding new ones. Form LinkedIn groups around your specialist subject; or, if you are a professional selling creative services, check out the new Creative Portfolio Display application (linkd.in/deDVX1), which aims to "empower creative professionals by creating a one-stop solution for maintaining their work portfolio and broadcasting it to millions".

● Cost: free (option to upgrade to a business account, which is a paid-for package)

- -

TIP: Top tips from LinkedIn

Present a full picture of yourself
Make sure you add a professional picture so people can easily recognise you and take some time to complete your profile. You'll show up in more search results the more information you provide about your experience and skills. While doing this, picture yourself at a conference or client meeting. How do you introduce yourself? That's your authentic voice and that's what should come across in writing.

Build connections
Connections are one of the most important aspects of your brand – the company you keep reflects the quality of your brand. Identify connections that will add to your credibility and pursue them.

Write a personal tagline
The line of text under your name is the first thing people see in your profile. It follows your name in search hit lists. It's your brand. Ensure it's something that at a glance describes who you are.

Put your elevator pitch to work
Go back to your conference introduction. That 30-second description, the essence of who you are and what you do, is a personal elevator pitch. Use it in the Summary section to engage readers. You've got 5-10 seconds to capture their attention.

Point out your skills
Think of the Specialties field as your personal search engine optimiser, a way to refine the ways people find and remember you. Mention particular abilities and interests, even a note of humour or passion.

Explain your experience
Briefly say what the company does. After you've introduced yourself, describe what you do and what your company does. Use those clear, succinct phrases here.

Distinguish yourself from the crowd
Use the Additional Information section to round out your profile with a few key interests. Maybe you belong to a trade association or an interest group; if you're an award-winner, add prestige by listing that here.

Ask and answer questions
Thoughtful questions and useful answers build your credibility. Make a point of answering questions in your field to establish your expertise and raise your visibility. You may need answers to a question of your own later on.

Recommendations
Pat your own back and others too. Get recommendations from colleagues and clients who will speak credibly about your performance and make meaningful comments when recommending others.

Source: LinkedIn
www.linkedin.com

Flickr

Join www.flickr.com and promote yourself visually by uploading photos of you and your products or service, and maybe even a few shots of happy customers. The site also carries video clips so you can show:

- events you host, speak at, or attend

- products you make (the finished product) as well as images of the production process

- happy customers wearing/using/enjoying your products and services

- your workspace

- your family (if you – and they – feel comfortable showing your personal side).

You can also easily pull the photos into your blog and social media pages.

- Cost: free (option to upgrade to a pro account which is a paid-for package)

YouTube

YouTube is the world's most popular online video community, with 24 hours of video uploaded every minute. Start your own business channel for free, and upload videos profiling you and your work. Create an account (www.youtube.com/create_account), start a channel (advice via YouTube video!), and start broadcasting to the world. You can give each of your videos a name and assign keywords to it to help with searching, plus you can have a short description of your company on your profile page. Again, these clips are very easy to add to your website, and they help keep the content fresh and interesting. Footage can even be filmed for free if you have a webcam in your laptop.

- Cost: free

Total budget required for online promotion: £0

Measure the results

Time to measure what's working and what's not. Measure media and press mentions through signing up to Google Alerts – and you'll be pleased to know there's a whole host of tools that are free to use and will show real-time results for what's working on your site and across social media profiles.

Look out, in particular, for the sources of your traffic (which are your highest referring sites) and your most popular pages. You can see days where your site receives spikes in visitor levels (and track this back to marketing) and measure if visitors are spending longer periods on the site and which times are popular, e.g. weekends, evenings, lunchtimes, etc.

Google Analytics offers intelligence on your website traffic and marketing effectiveness: www.google.com/analytics

There are other analytics options:

- Alexa – web traffic metrics, site demographics and top URL listings. www.alexa.com

- Clicky – monitors and analyses your site traffic in real time. www.getclicky.com

- Crazy Egg – see which pages visitors are visiting, with a colourful heat map. www.crazyegg.com

- Opentracker – gather and analyse web stats and monitor online visitors.
  www.opentracker.net

- StatCounter – an invisible web tracker and hit counter that offers data in real time.
  www.statcounter.com

- Urchin – this is the tool we use to measure and monitor traffic to Enterprise Nation. It is now owned by Google.
  www.urchin.com

- Website Grader – generates a free marketing report that compares your site with a competitor's.
  www.websitegrader.com

Hopefully what you will see is an upward curve of visitors and time spent on the site.

If you're selling anything, then hopefully this means more sales. And if your site is the business, this means you're in a strong position to attract advertisers and begin doing affiliate deals (see pages 112–5).

Checklist: Your social network

Task	Completed?
Presence on Twitter	
Profile on LinkedIn	
Account on Facebook	
Content uploaded to YouTube/Flickr	
Measuring online results	

Week 10

How to grow the business without outgrowing the home

With marketing and sales underway, you are getting known and making money. It's time to grow profits by focusing on what you do best and outsourcing the rest. It's perfectly possible to achieve this and manage an expanding team from your own small office/home office.

Team Work Saves Time

The business is growing, time is your most precious resource and you are in need of help. The quickest and most affordable place to get it is from other companies with whom you can partner to get projects done, as well as from accredited advisors who will offer advice on how the business can continue to grow.

With outsourcing you can free yourself up to dedicate your attention to sales, strategy or whatever the business activity is that you do best. My advice to all businesses is always: *focus on what you do best and outsource the rest*.

What can be outsourced, and to whom?

Admin

Hire a VA (virtual assistant) to do the admin tasks you don't want or don't have the time to do. Visit VA directories and resources to find your perfect match.

- International Association of Virtual Assistants
  www.iava.org.uk

- Society of Virtual Assistants
  www.societyofvirtualassistants.co.uk

- Time Etc
  www.timeetc.co.uk

- VA Success Group
  www.vasuccessgroup.co.uk

- Virtual Assistant Chamber of Commerce
  www.virtualassistantnetworking.com

- Virtual Assistant Coaching & Training Company
  www.vact.co.uk

- Virtual Assistant Forums
  www.virtualassistantforums.com

PR, marketing and design

Outsource your PR to a specialist who can be pitching and promoting the business whilst you're at work. Find skilled professionals on directory sites such as Bitsy (www.bitsythis.com) and Business Smiths (www.businesssmiths.co.uk) or contact companies such as PrPro.

- Bitsy
  www.bitsythis.com

- Business Smiths
  www.businesssmiths.co.uk

- PrPro
  www.prpro.co.uk

See pages 120–1 for top PR tips from PrPro's Louise Findlay-Wilson.

Sales

Hire a sales expert to make calls, set up appointments and attend trade shows. Find these professionals on Bitsy (www.bitsythis.com), contact telemarketing companies that offer outbound sales calls as a service, or look at sales specialists such as Inside and professionals like Jackie Wade.

- Great Guns
  www.greatgunsmarketing.co.uk

- Inside
  www.theinsideteam.co.uk

- Winning Sales
  www.winningsales.co.uk

See pages 104–5 for advice from Jackie on how to warm up for a cold call.

Customer service

Looking after your customers is vital, but even that can be outsourced to great effect. Get Satisfaction's tagline is "people-powered customer service" – it provides a web-hosted platform, much like a forum, where customers can ask questions, suggest improvements, report a problem or give praise. It can save you time and money by making customer service an open process that leverages the wisdom of crowds.

Questions are answered by other users, rather than you as the site host. You don't want to outsource this completely as it's good to show personal contact with customers, but this is a useful tool that could improve your business as customers offer their feedback.

- www.getsatisfaction.com

IT

Spending too many hours trying to fix a single IT problem? Outsource the hassle and save your time, money and blood pressure. Find IT professionals on Bitsy or contact IT support teams connected to the large retailers.

- Geeks-on-Wheels
  www.geeks-on-wheels.com

- The TechGuys
  www.thetechguys.com

- The Geek Squad
  www.geeksquad.co.uk

Tech support

 Check out EasyTech, a range of Staples products that will help you set up your computer and keep it working like new.

Accounts

Unless you are in the accountancy business, this is almost a must to be outsourced. Monthly payroll, accounts, VAT returns and corporate tax returns all take time and it's time you can't afford or simply don't have. A cost/benefit analysis is likely to show that it's cheaper to outsource to a qualified accountant. Ask around for recommendations of accountants in your area who deliver a quality service at a competitive cost and are registered with the Institute of Chartered Accountants in England and Wales. On page 49 is a listing of sites you can visit to identify accountants in your area.

For online accounting and invoicing that makes life easier for you and your accountant, check out:

- FreeAgent
  www.freeagentcentral.com

- KashFlow
  www.kashflow.co.uk

- Liquid
  www.liquidaccounts.net

- QuickBooks
  www.quickbooks.co.uk

- Sage One
  www.sageone.com/accounts

And keep track of invoices with the template provided on page 180.

Steps to successful outsourcing

Do the groundwork

Spend some time working on the task yourself so that you've built some foundations before handing it over to a third party. For example, if you outsource sales then have a ready-made contacts list and some open doors that the specialist can build on, rather than starting from scratch. This will make it more cost-effective for you and means they hit the ground running; it's not a contract from a cold start, you have already done the groundwork.

Be clear on the brief

Having spent some time doing the task yourself, you will have a clear idea of the brief. Back to the example of outsourcing sales, if you've spent 6–12 months sourcing leads and making contacts, you'll have a much clearer idea of the type of prospecting the specialist should do.

The clearer the brief, the better the results.

Take your time

And take references. Spend time evaluating the specialists in the market and, if you can, talk to their existing clients. Do they have the industry experience you're after? Will they represent your brand in a professional manner? Have they shown commitment to other clients? When an outsourced arrangement works well, the partner becomes part of your team so choose them as carefully as you would choose an employee.

Let go!

Outsourcing a key function means having to let go a little. Someone else becomes accountable for these results. Embrace this rather than resist it. As the business owner you remain in ultimate control but the expert will need their own space in which to flourish. Outsourcing can save you time and help make you money. Finding the right partner, on the right terms, will make you feel like a new and liberated person.

- -

TIP: The web's friendliest business-to-business marketplace

We created Bitsy, the friendliest business-to-business marketplace on the web, in response to seeing so many small businesses wanting to outsource and subcontract work to others. What makes Bitsy such a good place to look for these kinds of suppliers is its blog and its community. Bitsy rewards its best suppliers with profile on its blog, and its community lets it know who gets the thumbs up and who gets the thumbs down, by posting reviews and feedback on suppliers' pages and in the forums.

- www.bitsythis.com

- -

CASE STUDY

Name: Tim Latham
Business: Unconsultancy
Started: January 2010

Tim Latham had been a small business owner for ten years when he came up with the idea for new business, Unconsultancy.

"I had looked around for clear thinking and intellectually rigorous advice for small businesses and was disappointed with what I found. What I am seeking to do with Unconsultancy is make available high quality assistance to entrepreneurs and small business owners. I work with some clients as their general business mentor or 'the co-founder they don't have' but most of my work is helping owners really understand their business model. When you can properly describe your model, you're far better equipped to improve performance and success."

Tim's background has involved working for some large organisations including the Royal Air Force, Shell, and PricewaterhouseCoopers. Yet what Tim is now relishing is the freedom of running his own business and being able to act and move at speed.

"I can have an idea in the morning, work on it over a couple of coffees and implement it by teatime! This could have taken months or years to implement in big companies, so the best thing about moving to run a smaller company has been the ability to get things done quickly – but of course I'm only paid if I have clients!"

Tim is promoting the business online and off by speaking at events, hosting workshops, regular blogging and having a presence on Twitter and Facebook. Rather than hire full-time employees to help out on projects and assist with his own business growth, Tim prefers to outsource to other self-employed professionals who can do the job more cost effectively, and share Tim's ethos and passion for the subject.

As word of Unconsultancy is spreading to more businesses, Tim is receiving increasing requests to run workshops. He has identified opportunities to advise new bodies being created on the back of government policies and programmes. The plan is to grow the business and continue researching the latest thinking in business strategy, bringing it to small enterprises in a digestible form.

"I'm waiting to hear about funding for a major research journey to Silicon Valley, Seattle and Pittsburgh to look at some of the USA's engines of innovation and to hopefully bring some of that learning back to UK businesses. The next 12 months look very bright indeed."

- **www.unconsultancy.com**
  @unconsultancy

Form teams

Once you've chosen your outsourced partner(s), it's important to keep in regular contact and work together as a team. There are a number of online project management and collaboration tools to help you stay on top of projects and in control of the company.

Basecamp
The project management tool we rely on at Enterprise Nation. This is a top-class product that allows you to create projects, invite people to view them, upload files and make comments. It's effective online project management that can be accessed from anywhere.

- **www.basecamphq.com**

Google Docs
Share documents via Google with GoogleDocs. You can edit on the move, choose who accesses documents and share changes in real-time.

- **docs.google.com**

Huddle
Offers simple and secure online workspaces. Huddle is hosted, so there's no software to download and it's free to get started.

- **www.huddle.com**

Solutions to enable group-talk

GoToMeeting
Work with anyone, anywhere with this easy to use online meeting tool.

- **www.gotomeeting.com**

Ketchup

Share and record meeting notes.

- www.useketchup.com

Pow Wow Now

Free conference calling at 'open access' level. Priced packages available.

- www.powwownow.co.uk

Skype

Free and easy-to-use conference calls for Skype users.

- www.skype.com/allfeatures/conferencecall

TIP: Help from an entern

If you have a project requiring specialist skill or attention consider hiring an entern. Enterns are enthusiastic students and graduates, passionate about entrepreneurship and looking for work experience in young start up companies.

- www.enternships.com

Form partnerships

If relationships with other companies and self-employed professionals develop, you may decide to form a partnership. Consider writing a partnership agreement as your 'pre-nup' in business. At the outset of a relationship, all is good and you're excited about the potential, but it's best to be safe; have a few things written and agreed so all parties are clear on expectations.

The following should not be taken as concrete legal advice, more of a guideline on how to draw up an agreement. An agreement need only be a single page and cover the basics:

Scope of agreement

What is your partnership working to achieve? For example, "This agreement is made between Company A and Company B. The agreement is related to the generation of online advertising revenues/hosting of an event/development of a new product."

Respective responsibilities

Set out the expectations on who does what. For example, Company A will be responsible for promotion and business development and Company B will take on technical development and client care. Also include a note of how you'll keep each other briefed, maybe through the use of an online project management tool such as Basecamp.

Finances

What will be the split in revenue, and is this before or after costs? And who owns the intellectual property of the product/service/activity? Consider including a clause that states the agreement will be reviewed in six months so that both parties can check on progress and have the right to cease the agreement if it hasn't gone as planned.

Be fair

Agreements where both parties feel they're receiving their fair share are likely to be longer-lasting than those when one party feels embittered. Talk about this before writing and concluding the agreement. Make sure there's no resentment or sense of being exploited on either side.

Sign it!

After making effort to produce an agreement, be sure to sign it! And then store it so you can access it easily if the need arises.

When writing the clauses in your agreement, think about all the things that could go wrong and safeguard against them. It's a practical exercise and won't harm your newly formed business relationship but will get it off on a firm footing. If you're looking for a template agreement, check out the following sites:

- Click Docs
  www.clickdocs.co.uk

- Off to see my lawyer
  www.offtoseemylawyer.com

Speaking of partnerships, maybe you're considering going into business with your other half. It's something I see happen a lot. I also see how business brings couples closer together. It's an arrangement that's working well for John and Moi Lakey.

CASE STUDY

Name: John and Moi Lakey

Business: Candlelight Creations

Started: January 2010

The journey of Candlelight Creations began for John and Moi Lakey in early 2010 when the couple were making playful sock creatures for five-year-old son, Sam. The creative couple soon realised that others might like to do the same with their children.

"So taking our existing business and creative skills, we put together ten designs, created a basic product and took it to market."

The aim was to sell the sock product to the retail trade, so John and Moi hired a designer and had professional boxes and booklets produced. The next step was to approach retailers with their offer. After "persistent pestering" (John's words!) they managed to secure a meeting with the Eden Project, who placed an order on that very day!

"We knew then that we had a winning product. This gave us the confidence to target other retail outlets. Our approach is to send samples and follow up ten days later with a telephone call to get feedback. So far this has worked well for us. We are picking up retail outlets week on week and sometimes they call us within the ten days to talk more about the product."

To promote the business and raise awareness, the company also entered 'The Pitch', which has become Britain's biggest pitching competition. The company is through to the finals, and as well as introducing them to new people it has helped them to perfect their business plan, having had to pitch it to others!

John and Moi work together from home in a large workshop. They have recognised each other's weaknesses and strengths and work around them.

"We don't forget to have fun and time away from work together. As we have a child as well, the work needs to be shared. School runs and cooking gets shared and it is definitely not a nine-to-five job. But we love what we do and think that it is a good education for our son to be brought up surrounded by an interesting and exciting business!"

Plans over the next 12 months include releasing more products on the same line, with Moi creating the product and John working on production and sales. "The future looks exciting," says John.

As for advice for couples considering starting a business together, the happy and industrious couple have this to say:

"For any partners looking at going into business together, make sure that you share the same dream. You also need a strong relationship and to be able to identify each other's strengths and weakness. But most of all ... do it!"

- **www.candlelight-creations.com**
  @johnlakey

On the Move

In week 5 we heard how to find the right technology for your office and now it's time to meet up with partners and take that technology outside! With a few simple tips and tricks you can enjoy unprecedented flexibility, and work almost anywhere: from your local coffee shop to the public park.

Here's how to keep your enterprise on the go away from the office.

With your computer

If you already have a fairly up-to-date laptop computer, you have much of what you really need to work on the move. Most can pick up wireless internet access from receivers already built-in. But if you have a slightly older laptop you can buy a small adaptor which you plug into a spare USB port. Affordable options are available from a company called Belkin (www.belkin.com/uk), who provide pretty clear instructions to help you get started.

The other thing to invest in might be a spare battery. Some modern laptops (particular netbooks) have such long battery life that this might not be necessary, but it's good to have as a back-up.

Accessing Wi-Fi hotspots

Nowadays, if you use your laptop computer in a public place like a coffee shop, a library, or even some public parks, you'll find that you can connect to a Wi-Fi hotspot. These are wireless internet connections that allow you to surf the web, check your email and instant message when you're away from your home office.

Unless you've a kindly local council who'll provide Wi-Fi hotspots free of charge, the chances are the hotspots you'll come across will cost you something. They usually charge for an hour's access, for 24 hours or for a month at a time and prices do vary. But at the time of writing, the three main providers of wireless internet access are BT, a company called The Cloud and T-Mobile.

- BT Openzone
  www.btopenzone.com

- The Cloud
  www.thecloud.net

- T-Mobile HotSpot
  www.t-mobile.co.uk

TIP: Free hotspots

Wi-Fi hotspots are usually free of charge in public libraries, where you'll have to be a member. Another, rather more tasty, option is independent coffee shops, where owners encourage you to use their hotspots to boost sales of their goods. Coffee shop chains like Starbucks and Costa usually have deals with third party providers such as The Cloud and T-Mobile, which can be quite expensive. If you can't see a sign in the window, just ask your local coffee shop owner. And if they don't have Wi-Fi, and if enough people ask, they might just get it installed!

Use MyHotspots to find your nearest WiFi locations.

- MyHotspots
  www.myhotspots.co.uk

With your mobile phone

Smartphones are one of the most popular devices for working on the move. With it in hand, you can surf the web, check email and edit some office documents. Tracy Gray runs specialist jewellery company Button and Bean, with help from her BlackBerry.

> "I can accept orders, answer customer queries, check accounts and do a host of other things on my phone that traditionally I'd have to do whilst sat at a PC.

> "In business I think the single most important thing to consider is customer service. It's so important to communicate with customers and respond quickly to their enquiries and, sometimes, their problems. From years spent in customer service I learned that a customer with an issue is a real opportunity to show them how important they are. And this can be achieved simply by calling and listening to them.

> "My BlackBerry helps me run the business more effectively, but it also allows me to work on the move which is very useful when I'm out with my girls on Mummy duty!"

Watch Tracy talk about her business and how technology helps at: bit.ly/hDjldd

Everything from anywhere

If you already use web mail, you'll be used to the idea of your messages and contacts being available from any computer connected to the internet. So, how about running your entire business from any computer anywhere?

Web applications are programs that are run online rather than on your computer alone. You run them through your web browser and all the data is stored on the internet so, in effect, you can use them and your information from pretty much any computer anywhere!

The best example is provided by Google, whose Google Apps offering includes email, instant messaging, a calendar, word processor, spreadsheet and presentation software, as well as a website builder.

All the work you do is stored on the internet so you can log in and out from anywhere and see the same information. Also, if your computer crashes or you buy a new system you won't lose any data or have to reinstall it on a new machine.

Google Apps is free to use and easy to set up.

- Google Apps
  www.google.com/a

Remote desktop

It is possible to access your files and folders with software such as GoToMyPC (www.gotomypc.com) or PCnow (pcnow.webex.com).

Week 11

Happy customers and balanced business – a recipe for success

In this final section and week we look at how to keep customers coming back, keep the business in balance and ensure you have all the support you need.

Attract Customers Back

You are making sales via your site and developing a strong community of fans and followers. Give visitors and customers a reason to return by following these steps.

Fresh and user-generated content

Encourage visitors and customers back to your site with regular posted content, and if it's an e-commerce site, keep the product range updated. Give your site some TLC each day, as fresh content will attract visitors who want to see what's new and will also appeal to the trawling web spiders who determine search engine results.

Encourage your site visitors to get to know each other through a forum, comment boxes or a plug-in application. Before you know it, a sense of community will develop and visitors will log on each day to find out who's saying what and what's happening with whom.

Exclusive offers

Extend offers to your existing customers, readers or members that will tempt them back. This offer could be conditional on customers referring a friend: that way your customer returns to the site with others in tow. Add to this with a badge of honour; design an icon that visitors can display on their own site to show their affiliation with you.

Guest appearances

Invite special guests to appear on your site via guest blog posts, hosting a webchat or a featured interview.

Keep in touch

Communicate all these good and 'sticky' things to your users through a regular e-newsletter powered by products such as MailChimp (www.mailchimp.com) or AWeber Communications (www.aweber.com).

Roya Dabir-Alai (in the next case study) knows her customers so well that she's often to be found at their weddings!

CASE STUDY

Name: Roya Dabir-Alai, Nicky Croxford and Trisha Champaneri
Business: Sitting in a Tree
Started: Summer 2007

Roya Dabir-Alai had made quite a name for herself amongst her friends by successfully introducing lots of happy couples to each other. With friends pointing out her uncanny knack for matchmaking, and Roya identifying a gap in the market for people serious about finding a relationship but not liking the available services, she decided to launch a company, Sitting in a Tree, in the summer of 2007.

"I had a steady stream of clients through friends but we really took off when I had my first piece of publicity – a full page article in the *Metro* (editorial, not advertorial). Everything spiralled from there and that's when my two colleagues Nicky and Trisha joined."

In February 2010 the team moved the company online in order to scale and grow. Being online meant the team not having to do as much (the matchmaking process now being automated) and numbers grew as the service was available at all hours. Roya and her partners were keen to maintain the feel of the company and they still wanted to keep it niche, maintaining quality and integrity. But now with less demanding roles in the business, the partners are free to pursue other projects, maintaining the site in their spare time. The team get together regularly for meetings and communicate mainly through telephone, email and text.

"Most of our promotion comes through press editorial and not a penny has been spent on marketing or advertising. I have been lucky to appear in lots of newspaper and magazine articles and I've been on the radio a few times. We are also fortunate to have many affiliations, for example being chosen for a BlackBerry small business project and sponsoring the singles' element of the Royal Parks Foundation half-marathon this year. For us, word of mouth is much more effective than anything else, as we want to grow organically. Most of our customers find us through friends."

A relationship with the site doesn't end when customers have found their perfect match. Roya has been to several weddings of Sitting in a Tree members, and couples email the team frequently to ask for advice.

"We have recently taken the decision to make the site totally free to users. We decided that the government austerity measures were depressing everyone and that the one thing everyone should be able to enjoy for free is love! I started this business because I believed in the idea. I still do. And it means a lot to me to help people find their perfect match and then maintain a close relationship with them. That's what good business is all about – providing a good service, time and time again!"

- **www.sittinginatree.co.uk**
  @sitinourtree

Keep the Business in Balance

As the business continues to grow, you will want to maintain momentum and grow at a comfortable pace. Achieve this by following what I call 'the golden triangle', which will keep you and the business in balance. This requires spending roughly a third of your time on three key things:

1. Customer care

Look after your customers by delivering a quality product or service, on time and within budget. And remember ... the customer is always right!

I ask clients for feedback so that I can keep a check on what they're thinking and changes they'd like to see. It's good to know some personal details about your customers, too. (Maybe the date of their birthday, their favourite hobby or names of their children.) As you gather these details, make a quick note so that you can send a birthday card on the right date, enquire after GCSE results at the right time, etc. Don't go overboard, but showing that you care certainly won't harm your relationship.

Offer customers good service, regular communication and an innovative line of products and services. It will stand you in good stead.

2. New business

Taking care of customers means taking care of sales. Why? Because it costs less to win business from existing customers than it does to find new ones. And if customers are happy, they'll say good things about you to new and potential customers. This is called word-of-mouth marketing and achieving it is every business owner's dream!

Secure new clients through marketing, encouraging recommendations and direct-sales calls and pitches.

3. Admin

Not as enjoyable as the first two, but it still has to be done. Keep the books in order by raising invoices in good time, being on top of cash flow and filing tax returns and company documents on time and in order. In short, keep the finances in check and the books up-to-date.

Cash is king

Keep an eye on the accounts so you can see how much money is in the bank, how much is owed and whether this covers your outgoings.

Invoices

Be on time with invoicing and keep a record of amounts outstanding. I have a simple spreadsheet with five columns labelled 'client', 'invoice amount', 'invoice number', 'date submitted' and 'date paid'.

See page 180 for a template invoice reporting sheet.

Your invoices should be a simple document with basic but thorough details. The less cause for question on the invoice, the faster it will be paid!

Settle invoices as promptly as you can. Your suppliers will be grateful and should repay you with good service.

You can balance the budget with a piece of accounting software. Priced at between £50 and £100 for 'starter' versions, these packages offer sales and expense tracking, invoice templates, bank reconciliations and basic bookkeeping. See page 160 for details of options.

Receipts

Keep business-related receipts in a place where they're easy to find. I have a big wicker box that doubles as a collecting place for receipts. It's helpful that they're all in one place when it's time to do the VAT return.

Right on time

Without the old framework of office life, you'll want to keep a grasp on time: planning it, tracking it, and definitely making the most of it. Do so with these on and offline technology solutions.

Freshbooks
An application that tracks the time you spend on projects and turns this into professional looking invoices. Particularly useful for businesses providing professional and business services.

- www.freshbooks.com

Remember the milk
Take your task list with you and add to it from anywhere with this nifty web-based task manager that synchs with Google Calendar, Twitter, BlackBerry, iPhone, instant messenger, email and text messages. The basic package is free.

- www.rememberthemilk.com

Other time tracking software
- Cashboard
  www.getcashboard.com

- Four Four Time
  www.fourfourtime.co.uk

- TraxTime
  www.spudcity.com/traxtime

If, like me, you're still a pen-and-paper person invest in a diary, filofax or wall calendar from a wide range of options from www.staples.co.uk.

• •

TIP: Bug business

Save time and keep customers happy by having bookings taken by a resource such as Booking Bug (www.bookingbug.com), an online service that allows you to take and manage bookings anytime and from anywhere.

• •

Sample invoice

1. Name of your contact

2. The date

3. An address to which the cheque shall be sent or bank details for accounts in which monies should be deposited

4. Company registration and VAT number

5. Invoice number or purchase order (PO) number

6. Payment terms (e.g. payable within 30 days of receipt)

7. A brief product description or summary of services

8. Amount owing (inclusive or exclusive of VAT, depending on whether you're registered).

I think it's good practice to include a cover note, too, that confirms what's being invoiced and thanks the client for their custom.

Invoice

Attention: Joe Smith
Managing Director
A. N. Other Small Business
321 First Street
Anytown, County AB1 2CD
Date 29/01/2011

Your small business address
123 Second Street
Anothertown, County AB2 3CD
T 01234 567 8910
F 01234 567 8911
you@youremailaddress.com
http://www.yourwebsite.com/

Your company registration
VAT no. 12345678910

PROJECT TITLE: A. N. Other Small Business website
PROJECT DESCRIPTION: Redesign of business website
INVOICE NUMBER: 01
TERMS: 30 days

Description	Amount owed
Graphic design	£1,500.00
Programming	£2,000.00
Hosting	£500.00
Total	**£4,000.00**

Please make cheque payable to Your Name and deliver to the
address printed on this invoice.

Sincerely yours,

Your Name

YOUR SMALL BUSINESS

Template 8: Invoice Management

Date	Client	Work	Amount (exclusive or inclusive of VAT)	Invoice no.	Date invoice sent	Date settled

Seek Help and Support

As a tweet to me once said "asking for help does not make you weak, but it could make you a success." Ask questions at every opportunity; of your peers, of mentors and accredited business advisors. Here's where to find them.

Peers

Who better to turn to than those who are also going through the experience of starting and growing a business? Visit the sites below and join their active forums and communities of business owners who will be more than happy to help.

- Business Zone
  www.businesszone.co.uk

- Start Up Donut
  www.startupdonut.co.uk

- Business Matters Magazine
  www.bmmagazine.co.uk

- Inafishbowl
  www.inafishbowl.com

- Enterprise Nation
  www.enterprisenation.com

Mentors

The coalition government has announced a national mentoring programme and the recruitment of no less than 40,000 mentors who will be on hand to help young and start-up businesses. Find out more on the link to the press release below. Details on how to find a mentor are still to come, but keep your eyes on the Department for Business, Innovation & Skills (BIS) at www.bis.gov.uk.

- '[Vince] Cable announces new business mentoring network'
  bit.ly/9mYTfC

• •

TIP: Support from The Supper Club

One of the most popular offers made on the launch of national campaign, StartUp Britain, was the offer of 1,000 mentoring hours from members of The Supper Club. Duncan Cheatle, founder of The Supper Club says:

> "Our members are successful business owners who are willing and able to help the next generation of entrepreneurs. They are doing this through offering their time and mentoring start ups via calls or meeting face-to-face. The purpose is for the start up to describe their business and outline aims, and for the more experienced business owner to offer feedback and direction. It's proving to be incredibly popular and is an effective way to transfer skills from one business owner to another."

● www.preludegroup.co.uk/what-we-do/start-up-britain

• •

Thoughts on a mentor

Over the ten-years-plus of running my own business, I have developed a view on mentors. It may not be a view with which you agree, as each business owner is different. But this is what has worked for me.

Don't restrict yourself to one mentor! I have learnt from many people as my businesses have passed through different stages of development. I would approach the person I felt best placed to have the answer, take on board their views, consider my options, and then act.

The ideal mentor is someone who possesses four things:

1. experience of your industry/sector

2. the ability to listen

3. the technical skills to advise

4. a willingness to make introductions to useful contacts.

If you can find these in one person, you are a fortunate person.

One of the finest things a mentor can do is allow you to talk. By doing so, you will often find you work out the answer. You sometimes just need a sounding board to answer your own question.

Accredited advisors

When starting and growing your business, consider approaching your local enterprise agency for support. The National Federation of Enterprise Agencies acts as an umbrella organisation for all agencies so you can find your local contact at www.nfea.com.

Local business advisors can help with everything from business planning to applying for funds and financial forecasting.

StartUp Britain

In March 2011 a national campaign was launched to encourage more people to start a business and support existing businesses to grow. The campaign is run by a team of eight business owners and entrepreneurs, with support from the government and a number of corporate sponsors.

The face of the campaign is a website which offers links to useful resources and content, as well as valuable offers from large corporates and leading brands. Visit the site to be inspired and to celebrate the start-ups of Britain.

- www.startupbritain.org

Enterprise Nation

Turn to Enterprise Nation as your central resource and friend in business. Every month we:

- profile small business success stories

- release eBooks on topics that matter most

- produce videos with bite size business advice

- host webchats with experts and special guests

- develop new tools to help you increase sales and reduce costs

- connect you to peers via forums and our friendly marketplace.

Enterprise Nation is the place where you can access advice and support, raise profile and make sales.

- www.enterprisenation.com
  @e_nation

Partners

Meet the three companies delivering StartUp Saturday to you:

Staples

Staples is the world's largest office products company and is committed to helping start ups and small business. It not only sells technology, office furniture and stationery but offers a wide range of business services. Staples is the host of StartUp Saturday with weekly classes held in its UK stores from 9.30am until 10.30am. The company is also making special offers on essential items from business cards to laptops.

To find out more about Staples call into your local store or visit www.staples.co.uk.

Enterprise Nation

Enterprise Nation is a small business support company offering books, kits, online tools, content, friendly forums, video clips and weekly courses designed to help anyone start and grow a small business. Enterprise Nation has produced the content for StartUp Saturday and provides a home on the web for your questions and ongoing support after completing your course.

www.enterprisenation.com

CragRats

CragRats is a specialist training company that draws on a unique mix of live theatre, dynamic workshops and video based learning. The company and its trainers are responsible for delivering the fun and friendly weekly StartUp Saturday class. CragRats is the only training company whose enterprise programmes are accredited by City & Guilds.

www.cragrats.com

Conclusion

This brings us to the end of the workbook.

I hope this StartUp Saturday step-by-step guide has pointed you in the right direction and prepared you with all you need to get your start up off the ground.

Hopefully one thing that has repeatedly come across is the sheer number of people and resources out there that are on your side, not least:

- the websites that are home to communities of small business owners who will help

- the private sector companies coming up with products and services to make your life easier

- the national campaign that will listen to your views and represent them to government.

In whichever direction you turn, you will find answers and you will find others to cheer you along, including your fellow StartUp Saturday start ups.

If you came along to any of the sessions, please keep in touch with classmates, and be sure to let me know how you get on. Maybe next year you'll be returning to StartUp Saturday, or appearing as a case study in this book, to tell the story of how you travelled from start up to business success!

Best wishes,

Emma Jones

Other books from Brightword

Brightword is a publisher specialising in kits, books and eBooks for small businesses and start ups.

Twitter your Business (eBook)
by Mark Shaw

The real value of Twitter is in the ability to search for real people talking about real stuff, right now and in real time. This offers individuals, businesses and brands the opportunity to stop talking *at* customers and start talking *with* customers. A subtle but huge difference.

This is the definitive guide to doing so, and to adding significant value to your business through Twitter. It is written by the UK's foremost Twitter consultant and commentator.

Go Global (Paperback and eBook)
by Emma Jones

In this book, bestselling author Emma Jones puts paid to perceptions that global trade is beyond small businesses and sole traders. She shows that you don't need big budgets or to be a big business to be a globally successful one. She offers a route map that will have your start up trading across the globe and illustrates how it can be done, with stories from 20 successful small exporters.

The Business Bites eBooks

Advanced guides to finance, selling, marketing and management of your start up. Each 'bite' is written by an expert and experienced entrepreneur, and provides all the advice and inside tips you need to keep your small business one step ahead of the rest. New titles added monthly.

Sponsored by BlackBerry.